More Advanced Robotics with Lego® MindStorms™

Other titles of interest

BP901   Introducing Robotics with Lego MindStorms

* * * * *

BP450   How to Expand and Upgrade Your PC
BP467   How to Interface PCs
BP470   Linux for Windows Users
BP479   How to Build Your Own PC
BP484   Easy PC Troubleshooting

* * * * *

BP394   Programming Visual BASIC for Windows
BP444   Windows 98 Explained

* * * * *

BP394   An Introduction to PIC Microcontrollers
BP444   Practical PIC Microcontroller Projects

More Advanced Robotics with Lego® MindStorms™

Robert Penfold

Bernard Babani (publishing) Ltd
The Grampians
Shepherds Bush Road
London W6 7NF
England

Please note

Although every care has been taken with the production of this book to ensure that any projects, designs, modifications, and/or programs, etc., contained herewith, operate in a correct and safe manner and also that any components specified are normally available in Great Britain, the Publisher and Author do not accept responsibility in any way for the failure (including fault in design) of any projects, design, modification, or program to work correctly or to cause damage to any equipment that it may be connected to or used in conjunction with, or in respect of any other damage or injury that may be caused, nor do the Publishers accept responsibility in any way for the failure to obtain specified components.

Notice is also given that if any equipment that is still under warranty is modified in any way or used or connected with home-built equipment then that warranty may be void.

© 2000 BERNARD BABANI (publishing) LTD

First Published - December 2000

British Library Cataloguing in Publication Data
A catalogue record for this book is available from the British Library

ISBN   0 85934 902 0

Cover Design by Gregor Arthur
Printed and bound in Great Britain by Bath Press

Preface

At a first glance I suppose the LEGO MindStorms Robotics Invention System seems to be a fairly "run of the mill" construction kit, but the truth of the matter is very different. The RCX unit distinguishes the MindStorms kit from the rest of the field. It is an outsize Lego brick that has a display, control buttons, and crucially, it is fitted with a microcontroller. In other words, it has its own built-in computer chip that enables the completed robots to "think" for themselves. Instead of just going round in circles or backwards and forwards, finished models can perform pre-programmed routines, react to input from their sensors, and (or) they can be controlled manually from a PC via an infrared link. Using the latest add-on kit your robots can even "see" via a camera, and they can actually react to what they "see"!

A great deal can be achieved using nothing more than the Lego Robotics Invention System and a suitable PC, but with the aid of Lego's own accessories and some do-it-yourself add-ons it is possible to greatly extend the possibilities. Using a conventional programming language instead of RCX code it is possible to extend the capabilities of the robots still further. This book is for those who have mastered the fundamentals of the Robotics Invention System, and wish to progress further. It covers do-it-yourself topics such as building your own connectors and sensors, and using the Lego accessories that are available. The Lego sensors covered are an extra light sensor, the angle (rotation) and temperature types, and the vision system (Vision Command). Using an additional motor is also covered. The do-it-yourself sensors include light types, sound and temperature sensors, and a simple ultrasonic ranging system.

In order to construct all the robots featured in this publication it is necessary to build the do-it-yourself sensors and buy some additional Lego components. However, apart from these items the robots require no components that are not part of the standard Robotics Invention System. Some of the technical information is aimed at those with some experience of electronic circuits, but building and using the sensor designs is within the capabilities of beginners. Where possible, programs are given in both RCX code and Visual BASIC versions, but in a few cases only one programming language or the other is suitable. It is assumed that the reader has at least a basic understanding of RCX code, but no prior knowledge of Visual BASIC and conventional programming is assumed.

Robert Penfold

IMPORTANT

Lego MindStorms kits are not recommended for younger children, so any "under-age" MindStorms enthusiasts should always enlist the assistance of an adult when making any home-made connectors or if using a soldering iron or other tools.

TRADEMARKS

UNOFFICIAL GUIDE

TRADEMARKS

LEGO®, Mindstorms,™ and Vision Command™ are registered trademarks or trademarks of the Lego group of companies. All other product and brand names may be registered and legally protected trademarks of the companies that manufacture those products. There is no intent to use any trademarked name generically or to infringe that trademark in any way, and the names are only used in an editorial or literary context. Readers are advised to fully investigate ownership of a trademark before using it for any purposes.

To aid readability of this book, the trademark symbols ™ and ® are used initially, but not at every occurrence of the trademark name. This does not imply in any way that the name may not be a trademark or registered trademark.

Visual BASIC and VBA are registered trademarks of Microsoft Corporation

Delphi is a trademark of Borland International Corporation

Pentium is a registered trademark of Intel Corporation

UNOFFICIAL GUIDE

Neither the Author or Publishers of this book are connected or supported in any way by any Lego group company, and this book should not be confused with any publication that may be produced by a Lego group company.

Contents

1

Spirit.OCX 1

2

Using Visual BASIC 31

3

Making Connections 51

Spirit.OCX

Beyond RCX code

The Robotics Invention System does, of course, come complete with its own easy to use programming software. This enables people with no programming experience at all to program Lego MindStorms robots to undertake simple tasks. You produce a diagram that contains the various steps such as switch on motor A, wait for the light level to exceed 60 percent, etc., and from this flowchart the software generates the program for the RCX unit. Many programmers produce a flowchart first and then use this as an aid to writing the final program. RCX code frees the user from having to produce a conventional program, and from having to learn a conventional programming language. Practically anyone can produce simple programs straight away, and a couple of mouse "clicks" is all that is needed to download them to the RCX unit.

RCX code is certainly easy to learn and use, but a simple programming environment of this type will inevitably have some limitations. The most obvious one is that anything beyond fairly simple programs tends to become unwieldy, taking up a great deal of virtual screen space. Another common criticism of RCX code is that it does not have provision for variables. A variable is simply a value that is stored in memory, but it is not a fixed quantity, and can be altered as and when necessary. RCX code does actually have a counter that can be used as a very basic variable, but it offers nothing beyond this. The lack of variables may seem to be a minor point, but it can be a major drawback.

Versions 1.0 and 1.5 of the Robotics Invention System are not supplied with any form of conventional programming language. This seems likely to change with version 2.0, with its assembler and scripting languages, but in the mean time versions 1.0 and 1.5 are supplied with an ActiveX control called Spirit.OCX that enables MindStorms robots to be programmed from conventional Windows programming languages. This method is now well established, and seems likely to remain popular with MindStorms enthusiasts for some time to come. It is probably possible to use Spirit.OCX with any of the main Windows programming languages, but in this publication we will only consider its use with Microsoft's Visual BASIC, and the broadly similar VBA (Visual BASIC for Applications).

Spirit.OCX?

Exactly what does Spirit.OCX do? The subject of ActiveX controls is a complex one, but in this context the ActiveX control is used to provide the host programming language with a range of additional commands. A language such as Visual BASIC can undertake mathematics, produce onscreen graphics, handle scrollbars and other onscreen controls, and a great deal besides. This is all very useful, but when controlling a Lego robot you primarily need facilities to communicate with the robot via the infrared link, switch motors on and off, and this sort of thing. Spirit.OCX adds facilities of this type to the host programming language so that it can be used to produce sophisticated control programs for Lego robots.

In this chapter we will consider the additional commands that are provided by Spirit.OCX. You really need to have a basic grasp of these before trying any programming. Learning to use them should not be too difficult because many have direct equivalents in RCX code. In fact the more simple programs that utilize Spirit.OCX have more than a passing resemblance to equivalents written in RCX code. Chapter 2 covers the use of Spirit.OCX with Visual BASIC, and includes some simple demonstration programs. Several practical programs using Spirit.OCX and Visual BASIC are provided in the final chapters of this book.

Operating modes

When using Spirit.OCX and a programming language there are two modes of operation, which are the direct and indirect modes, which are also known as the immediate and delayed modes. The indirect mode is the one normally used with RCX code, where a program is downloaded to the RCX unit and then run within the RCX unit. In other words, you download a program to your robot which then runs the program, making it follow a line on the floor, do somersaults, or whatever. The PC takes no further part in things once the software has been downloaded. With the direct method the program runs within the PC, which communicates with the RCX unit via the infrared link. There is no program running within the RCX unit, and its instructions all come directly from the PC.

When using the indirect mode the Windows programming language is really nothing more than a means of downloading software to the RCX unit. You utilize the extra commands and facilities provided by Spirit.OCX, but most of the host programming language's capabilities are left unused. A fortunate consequence of this is that you do not have to be a particularly expert programmer in order to program the RCX unit in this way. A good knowledge of the extra instructions provided by Spirit.OCX is clearly essential, but you can get by with a fairly rudimentary understanding of Visual BASIC, Delphi, or whatever language you are using.

Using the direct mode is very different, and a better understanding of the programming language is required. At the most basic level, the direct mode simply provides a means of manually controlling a robot. Using on-screen slider controls and buttons you control the direction of the robot, its speed, etc. At a more advanced level, the infrared link is used to pass readings from the sensors to the computer, which then sends appropriate instructions back to the robot. This is similar to having a program running in the RCX unit, but the PC instead of the microcontroller in the RCX unit does the "thinking". In theory this enables more powerful control software to be used, because the super-powerful Pentium processor in the PC rather than the simpler processor in the RCX unit controls the robot. In practice this extra computing power may not be of any great advantage, and it also has to be borne in mind that communication by way of the infrared link introduces small delays that could be problematic.

Another way of handling things is to have the robot send sensor readings back to the PC where they are displayed onscreen. The robot's operator can then respond to this information, and can even control the robot "blind" if the information from the sensors is sufficiently detailed.

The commands

A wide range of instructions is available for programming the RCX unit, and it is not possible to give a detailed description of every single instruction here. This would be pointless anyway, since some of the available commands are of limited use for general programming, and are not the type of thing you will use initially. Accordingly, we will concentrate on the commands that are needed for everyday programming of your robots. There is no documentation for Spirit.OCX supplied with the Robotics Invention System, but there is a document in Adobe PDF (portable document format) called the Software Developer Kit (SDK) that is available from the Lego MindStorms web site. This provides a description of every command plus some general information, and it is something that anyone who will be using Spirit.OCX should download. If possible it should also be printed out so that it is handy for reference purposes whenever it is required.

Motor On/Off

One or more motors can be switched on or off using simple On and Off commands, as they can with RCX code. The numbers of the outputs to be changed are placed within double quotation marks. Outputs 0 to 2 correspond to outputs A to C of the RCX unit. The first of these examples will switch on outputs A and B, and the second will switch off outputs B and C:

```
Spirit1.On "01"
Spirit1.Off "12"
```

SetFwd/SetRwd

The direction of motors is not set using the On command, but is instead set using separate forward and reverse instructions. These are respectively SetFwd and SetRwd. They are used much like the on and off commands, with the outputs to be affected being specified in double quotation marks. These two examples set the motors on outputs A and C to go forwards, and the motor on output B to go in reverse:

```
Spirit1.SetFwd "02"
Spirit1.SetRwd "1"
```

Float

In addition to On and Off commands there is also a Float instruction. This switches off the affected motors, but it is not quite the same as the ordinary off command. With the float command the motors are stopped in a free running mode. If you run the simple test program that operates a motor briefly and then switches it off, the motor stops almost instantly. Trying the same thing but switching the motor off using a Float instruction results in the motor cruising to a halt. The motors are not truly locked in position by an Off command, but turning the shafts is quite difficult.

The motors are stopped in what is termed brake mode. An Off instruction places a short circuit across the motor, whereas a float instruction simply leaves the motor disconnected from the supply. When the shaft of the motor is turned, the motor operates in reverse as a dynamo. With a short circuit across the two terminals of the motor the current generated tries to operate the motor, but the movement produced by the current opposes the existing movement of the shaft. Hence a braking action is obtained. If you try turning the shaft of one of the motors with and without the short circuit present, the difference is unmistakable. This example sets outputs A and B to the float mode:

```
Spirit1.Float "01"
```

AlterDir

This command changes the direction of the specified motors. Unlike SetFwd and SetRwd this command is not setting a specific direction. Instead, it is simply making the new direction the opposite of whatever it happened to be before the command was issued. In most situations it is better to use the commands that set a specific direction, as this avoids the possibility of things getting out of kilter. This example reverses the direction of the motors on outputs A and C:

```
Spirit1.AlterDir "02"
```

Wait

The Wait instruction simply provides a pause in the program, and it is most commonly used to keep one or more motors switched on or off for a specified period. It can simply be used to provide a delay for the period specified directly in the command, but the delay can also be specified in other ways. The way in which the two parameters in this command function is shared with some other commands, so it is worth looking at this aspect of things in some detail.

The first parameter sets the source of the delay value, and there are 17 potential sources for the commands that use this system. However, most of these sources are inapplicable to most commands, and others are not the types of thing you would need very often, if at all. Probably the two most commonly used sources are constants and variables, which are selected using values of 2 and 0 respectively. A constant, also known as a literal, is simply the number given in the next parameter of the command. In this example, the first parameter is 2, meaning that the delay value is the constant given in the second parameter:

```
Spirit1.Wait 2, 100
```

The literal value is 100, giving a delay of one second. The allowable range of values in a constant depends on the command in use, but for a Wait instruction it can be any integer (whole number) from 1 to 32767. This gives a maximum delay of almost five and a half minutes, which should be more than adequate for the vast majority of practical applications.

Variables are something we will cover in more detail as and when necessary, but a variable is just a value stored in a memory location. In the case of the RCX unit there are 32 memory locations specifically set aside for storing variables, and these are numbered from 0 to 31. This command has zero as the first parameter and 12 as the second, and the delay will therefore be controlled by the value stored in variable number 12.

```
Spirit1.Wait 0, 12
```

The delay this provides depends on the value stored in variable number 12, and the program must have placed a suitable value in this variable before the Wait instruction is performed. This version of the Wait instruction is only used where the delay time will need to be changed from time to time while the program is running, and this is easily accomplished by altering the value stored in the variable.

Random

The Wait instruction produces a random delay if the first parameter is 4. The second parameter then sets an upper limit for the delay. For instance, this example produces a random delay of between one hundredth of a second and 10 seconds:

```
Spirit1.Wait 4, 1000
```

This may not seem to be very useful, but there are practical applications for randomness. If you go exploring and find yourself going round in circles or otherwise going over the same old ground time and time again, you will realise what you are doing and break out of the pattern. A rover style robot running a simple control program has no way of knowing whether it is wandering far and wide, or is stuck in a fixed search pattern. Adding a random element can help to avoid getting your robots "stuck in a rut". A random element is also an essential feature of some simple games and novelties that can be implemented using the Robotics Invention System.

SetPower

You are not limited to simply switching the motors on and off, and it is possible to adjust the power fed to the motors. There are eight power levels from 0 (minimum) to 7 (maximum). The three parameters in this command start with a list of the motors to be changed, and then the source of the new power setting is specified. Finally the power setting is provided, directly or indirectly. This example would therefore set the motors on outputs A and C at power level 3:

```
Spirit1.SetPower "02", 2, 3
```

In this version the power of outputs A and C is set to the value stored in variable 9:

```
Spirit1.SetPower "02", 0, 9
```

There are some important points to bear in mind when using power settings. Setting a power level does not in itself switch a motor on. This must be done previously or subsequently using the On command. Similarly, setting a power level of 0 does not switch a motor off. A power level of 0 gives a very low output power, but it does not cut off power to the motor altogether. Do not confuse power levels with speeds. Reducing a motor from full power to half power does not necessarily reduce its rotation speed by half. If the motor is only loaded very lightly there will be very little reduction in speed, but if it is loaded heavily it might actually grind to a halt. Often the only way to find the power settings that give the desired result is to use trial and error.

SetVar

We have seen that some commands can use the values stored in variables, but this is only of use if there are ways of setting and manipulating the values stored in variables. Setting a variable to a specific value is performed using the SetVar command, and this has three parameters. The first selects the variable to be altered, the second selects the source, and the third is the value itself or the exact source. In this example variable number 4 is set to a value of 1023:

```
Spirit1.SetVar 4, 2, 1023
```

The valid range of values for a variable is integers from –32768 to +32767. However, make sure that the values of variables are appropriate to any commands they will be used in. The Wait command can only be used with positive numbers for example, and output powers can only be from 0 to 7.

SumVar

This command adds the specified value to the contents of a variable. The result of the addition is stored in the variable. It operates in much the same way as SetVar, with the three parameters selecting the variable to be altered, the source of the value to be added, and then exact source. In the first example 100 is added to the contents of variable 20, and the result is stored in variable 20. If variable 20 originally contained 70, it would contain 170 after this instruction had been completed. The second example adds the contents of variable 8 to variable 22 and stores the result in variable 22. If variables 8 and 22 respectively contained values of 55 and 200, once the instruction had been completed they would contain 55 and 255.

```
Spirit1.SumVar 20, 2, 100
Spirit1.SumVar 22, 0, 8
```

In practice SumVar is unlikely to be used with large values, but if it is, make sure that the results of this command stay within the maximum permissible value of 32767. Adding (say) 25000 to 20000 will cause an overflow, and will not produce an answer of 45000.

SubVar

This is the subtraction equivalent of the SumVar command. It subtracts the indicated value from the specified variable, and stores the result in the variable. The first example subtracts 54 from variable 12. If variable 12 contained a value of 20 initially, it would contain –34 after this command had been performed. In the second example the contents of variable 23 are subtracted from the value stored in variable 16. The answer is stored in variable 16, and the value in variable 23 is unaffected. If variables 16 and 23 were respectively at values of 100 and 45 before the command was executed, they would be at values of 55 and 45 afterwards.

```
Spirit1.SubVar 12, 2, 54
Spirit1.SubVar 16, 0, 23
```

MulVar

DivVar

These two commands operate like SumVar and SubVar, but provide multiplication and division. The first example multiplies the value in variable 12 by the value in variable 22. If these two variables respectively contained 15 and 5 before the command was issued, they would contain 75 and 5 afterwards. The second example divides the value stored in variable 18 by 6. If variable 18 contains 39 before the command is executed, it will contain 6 afterwards. Where necessary, the answer is rounded down so that it is always an integer.

```
Spirit1.MulVar 12, 0, 22
Spirit1.DivVar 18, 2, 6
```

SgnVar

Using this command it is possible to test the sign of the value stored in a variable. It has three parameters, which are the variable used to store the result of the test, the source, which will usually be another variable, and the number of the variable to be tested. These are the three values that can be produced as a result of the test:

Value	Meaning
0	The variable is set at zero
1	The variable is set at a positive value
−1	The variable is set at a negative value

This example tests the value in variable 23 and places the result in variable number 4:

```
Spirit1.SgnVar 4, 0, 23
```

If the value in variable 23 was 18 when the command was issued, it would remain at this value afterwards, and variable 4 would be set to a value of 1.

AbsVar

This command places in the specified variable the absolute value of the number that is tested. In other words, it always produces a positive result regardless of whether the source value is positive or negative. For instance, this example would test the contents of variable number 24 and place the result in variable 20:

```
Spirit1.AbsVar 20, 0, 24
```

If variable 24 contained –101 before this command was issued, it would still contain –101 afterwards, and variable 20 would be set at a value of 101. If variable 24 contained 101, then variable 20 would still be set at 101.

AndVar

OrVar

These operate much like the other arithmetic commands, and they are used to provide bitwise AND and OR logical operations on the two values involved. Bitwise operations enable some bits of a binary number to be read or altered without reading or affecting other bits. This is not usually of great importance when dealing with the RCX unit, where there is individual control over each output, and there is no difficulty in reading just one of the three inputs. If you look at bitwise calculations using decimal numbers they do not make much sense. As a couple of examples, 255 AND 85 = 85, and 255 OR 85 = 255. To make sense of these bitwise operations the numbers have to be considered in their binary form. The 8-bit binary equivalents of 85 and 255 are 01010101 and 11111111. If we now look at our two examples again things are a little more logical

255	11111111
AND 85	01010101
Equals 85	01010101

There is only a 1 in the answer if there is a 1 in that column for both of the numbers being bitwise ANDed. By using a 0 in a certain column of one number, that column is set at 0 in the answer. Using a 1 in a certain column of one number sets the corresponding column of the answer at the same value used in the second source number. You can effectively eliminate certain bits of one number, by setting those bits at zero in the other number. This is a process usually referred to as masking.

255	11111111
OR 85	01010101
Equals 255	11111111

The bitwise OR process places a 1 in the answer if that bit is set at 1 in the first number, or the second number, or both. If you wish to make sure that a certain bit of a number is set at 1, but must avoid altering any of the other bits, bitwise ORing will do the trick. First produce a value that has the bit or bits to be altered set at 1 and all the other bits at 0. Then bitwise OR that value with the one that must be altered.

Flow control

Every program language requires commands that deal with flow control. On the face of it there is no need for any form of flow control, and a program can simply start at the beginning, go through a list of commands, and then stop. In practice it is hard to find applications where this sort of linear programming applies. When dealing with robots it is unusual for the robot to simply go through a series of commands and then stop. Even if the robot must perform some very simple production line task, having performed an action once, it must then go back to its original position and repeat the whole process over and over again. In terms of flow control, it simply entails going back to the beginning again once the end of the program has been reached. This repeating of a program, or part of a program, is known as looping. In some applications the robot must perform one task or another, depending on the data from a sensor. It is known as a branch when a program goes one way or another depending on the result of a decision-making instruction.

Loop

EndLoop

In order to repeat one or more commands a certain number of times it is just a matter of using the Loop command. Actually, a loop of this type requires two commands, which are Loop at the beginning of the loop and EndLoop at the end. The Loop command has two parameters that control the number of times the commands within the loop are performed. These point to the source of the value and the actual value in the usual way. The EndLoop command does not have any parameters. This routine will switch output A on and off 11 times:

```
Spirit1.Loop 2, 11
Spirit1.On "0"
Spirit1.Off "0"
Spirit1.EndLoop
```

This routine has the same effect, but the value stored in variable 27 controls the number of loops:

```
Spirit1.Loop 0, 27
Spirit1.On "0"
Spirit1.Off "0"
Spirit1.EndLoop
```

Sometimes you need the loop to carry on indefinitely, such as when monitoring a sensor for example. This is achieved by telling the loop to repeat zero times, as in this example, which will switch output A on and off indefinitely:

```
Spirit1.Loop 2, 0
Spirit1.On "0"
```

```
Spirit1.Off "0"
Spirit1.EndLoop
```

If

EndIf

On looking through the list of available commands when using Spirit.OCX you might come to the conclusion that there is no way of reading the sensors. There is a Poll command, but this is only usable as an immediate command that enables the program running in the PC to read a sensor. The normal way of handling a sensor is to read its value and place the result in a variable. A decision-making instruction then does one thing or another, depending on the value stored in the variable.

When using Spirit.OCX things are normally streamlined somewhat, and the decision-making instruction can directly read the sensor. Hence there are no separate instructions for reading the sensors. This aspect of things is handled by the flow control commands. Note though, that it is possible to do things the roundabout way if preferred, and the SetVar can set a variable to the value read from a sensor. A value of 9 is used to select a sensor as the source, and values of 0 to 2 respectively select sensors 1 to 3. This command would therefore set variable 10 to the value read from sensor 2 (input 3):

```
Spirit1.SetVar 10, 9, 2
```

Probably the most common way of reading a sensor is to use an If...EndIf routine. One or more commands are placed between the If and EndIf instructions, and these commands are only performed if a certain condition is met. There are five parameters in the If command, but none in the EndIf type which simply marks the end of the routine. The first two parameters point to a value using the standard type of source and precise source method. The final two values point to a second value using the same method. This leaves the middle parameter to define the type of test being performed, and these are the available options:

Number	Test Performed
0	>
1	<
2	=
3	<> (not equal)

Suppose that we required output A to be switched on if input 2 returns a reading that is greater than 50, this routine would provide the desired result:

```
Spirit1.If 9, 1, 0, 2, 50
Spirit1.On "0"
Spirit1.EndIf
```

The functions of the five parameters in the If command break down thus:

9   Read Sensor

1   number 1 (input 2)

0   If the returned value is greater than...

2   the constant value...

50   50, then perform these program lines…

In this case there is only one line of code to perform, which turns on output A. An EndIf instruction then terminates the routine. Of course, the first value in the comparison does not have to be a reading from a sensor, and the second value can be something other than a constant. It is quite acceptable to have an If instruction compare the values in two variables for instance.

Else

The If instruction is actually part of a standard If…Then…Else program structure, but the Else element is optional. In the previous example output A is switched on if input 2 returns a value that is more than 50, but the output is not switched off if the returned value is 50 or less. Output 2 is simply left in whatever state it had previously if the returned value is not greater than 50.

This version, which utilizes the If...Then...Else structure, will switch off the motor if the returned value is not greater than 50:

```
Spirit1.If 9, 1, 0, 2, 50
Spirit1.On "0"
Spirit1.Else
Spirit1.Off "0"
Spirit1.EndIf
```

The commands between the If and Else instructions are performed if the returned value is greater than 50, and those between the Else and EndIf instructions are performed for returned values of 50 or less. In this case there is only a single instruction in each section of the routine, but there can be numerous commands if necessary.

While

EndWhile

An If routine tests a sensor (or whatever) a single time and then moves on. It can be combined with a loop to perform the comparison a certain number of times, or it can be used with an infinite loop to keep on testing indefinitely. There is an alternative method of repeated testing in the form of the While and EndWhile instructions. These form what in conventional computing is called a do...while loop. In other words, an instruction or list of instructions is performed while a certain condition is met. There are five parameters in a While instruction, and these operate in the same way as the five parameters in an If instruction. This routine will keep switching output A on and off while the reading from input 1 is less than 75:

```
Spirit1.While 9, 0, 1, 2, 75
Spirit1.On "0"
Spirit1.Off "0"
Spirit1.EndWhile
```

SetSensorType

SetSensorMode

Before reading a sensor the sensor type and mode should be set using these commands. The SetSensorType command has two parameters, and the first of these selects the input for which the sensor type is being set. Values from 0 to 2 select inputs 1 to 3 respectively. The second parameter sets the type of sensor that the input will be set up to use, and numbers from 0 to 4 are used to handle five types. This table shows the type of sensor selected using each value:

Number	Sensor type
0	None
1	Switch (touch)
2	Temperature
3	Reflection (light)
4	Angle (rotation)

This instruction would set input 1 of the RCX unit for operation with a light sensor:

```
SetSensorType 0, 3
```

The SetSensorMode instruction is probably not necessary if the default settings of the selected sensor type are acceptable, but I always include it anyway. This ensures that data read from an input in always in the expected form. There are three parameters in the SetSensorMode command, and the first of these selects the input for which the mode is being set. This operates in the same way as the corresponding parameter in the SetSensorType instruction. The second parameter selects the mode, and the eight available modes are selected using values from 0 to 7. The table provided overleaf shows the available modes and the values that select them:

Number	Mode
0	Raw
1	Boolean
2	Transition counter
3	Periodic counter
4	Percent
5	Celsius
6	Fahrenheit
7	Angle

In raw mode the data is not manipulated in any way, and the returned value is the one returned from the analogue to digital converter in the RCX unit. This provides an integer in the range 0 to 1023. Boolean mode provides a reading of 0 or 1, and it is intended for simple sensors such as the touch variety where 0 and 1 respectively indicate that the sensor has not and has been activated. The transition counter mode is also for use with simple on/off sensors, and it counts the number of times that the signal from the sensor changes state. In other words, the count is incremented each time the sensor switches on or off. The periodic counter mode is similar, but it counts the number of complete on/off cycles. For example, on/off/on would give a count of three in the transition mode, as the input changes state three times during this sequence. There is only one complete on/off cycle, and the count would only be one in the periodic mode.

The percent mode gives readings from 0 to 100, and it is primarily intended for use with the light sensor. It can be used to good effect with other active sensors, including the home-made variety. This mode is not quite as straightforward as it might at first appear, and it is considered in more detail in subsequent chapters. The Celsius and Fahrenheit modes are only for use with the Lego temperature sensor, and they provide readings in the corresponding temperature scale. The angle mode is for operation with the Lego rotation sensor. This is a counter mode, and the value increments by one each time the monitored shaft rotates through 15 degrees in one direction. The count decrements by one each time the shaft goes through 15 degrees in the opposite direction. The rotation sensor is an optional extra, and it represents one of the most useful add-ons available for the Robotics Invention System.

Slope

The third and final parameter in a SetSensorMode command controls the slope used in Boolean mode. This is something that is not normally of any importance, and a value of 0 can be used to set normal operation. In the unlikely event that you wish to use something other than the standard slope characteristic a value from 1 to 31 is used. In order to understand the effect of the slope setting it is best to start by looking at the standard characteristic obtained using a value of 0. Figure 1.1 shows how the value returned from an input changes as the input voltage is steadily increased. The reading remains at zero until the input voltage reaches 55 percent of the full-scale voltage. The reading then changes to one, and remains at this value for higher input levels.

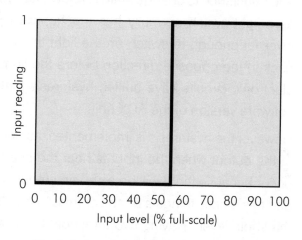

Fig.1.1 Input values for a rising voltage

The characteristic is slightly different when the input voltage is steadily reduced

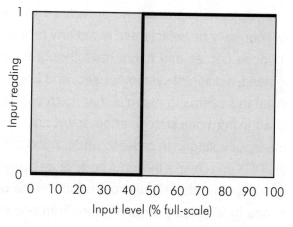

Fig.1.2 Input values for a falling voltage

back to zero. Figure 1.2 shows the input voltage versus reading for a decreasing input potential. This time the transition occurs at 45 percent of the full-scale voltage, and not at 55 percent. Having changed state, the reading is reluctant to change back again. Taking the input above 55 percent of the full-scale voltage takes the reading from zero to one, but taking the input level back below the 55 percent threshold does not set the reading back to zero. It has to be taken below 45 percent of the full-scale voltage. Having done this, it is then necessary to take the input back above the 55 percent threshold level in order to take the reading back to one again.

The reluctance to change state is known as hysteresis. An on/off switch such as a light switch normally has mechanical hysteresis. Having moved the lever far enough to switch on the light the lever then has to be moved well back in the opposite direction before the light is switched off again. Some electronic circuits have built-in hysteresis that gives the same effect as the software version of the RCX unit.

However the hysteresis is implemented, its purpose is to avoid rapid changes at the output when the input is near the changeover level. These changes occur because there will be a certain amount of noise present in the system, and this makes things a bit "hit or miss" when the input voltage is close to the threshold level. Having two threshold levels avoids this jitter, which may or may not cause problems if it is not suppressed.

The standard characteristic provides a moderate amount of hysteresis that will normally be sufficient to avoid any problems. Using a slope value of 1 to 31 does not, as one might have thought, control the amount of hysteresis. Instead, a different system is used, and Lego call this dynamic measurement. What this seems to mean is that no threshold voltages are used. Instead, a change from one state to another will only be produced by a rapid change in the input voltage. In order to understand this system you need to know that the RCX unit checks the input ports once every 3 milliseconds (0.003 seconds). A change in state will only be produced if the value returned from the converter jumps by a suitably large amount from one reading to the next.

If I am interpreting things correctly, it does not matter whether the change is positive or negative. A change in either direction will toggle the input value provided the change is large enough. The value in the slope parameter sets the minimum change needed to produce a change in the input value. For example, with a slope value of 20, a change in state will only be produced if the reading from the converter is at least 20 higher or lower than the previous reading.

The point of this system is that it ignores any gradual changes in the input voltage, but it responds to sudden changes even if they are relatively small. In Figure 1.3 the input voltage is changing by large amounts and with the standard method it would produce changes in output level. Even using a fairly small slope value it will fail

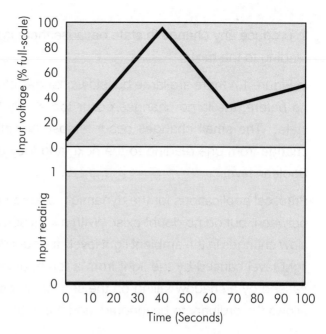

Fig.1.3 Large but slow changes at the input do not alter the Boolean level

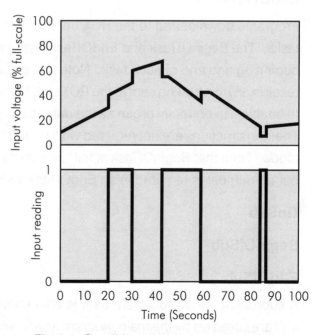

Fig.1.4 Small but rapid changes at the input do toggle the Boolean level

to produce any change in state because there is very little change from one reading to the next.

In Figure 1.4 there are large but slow changes plus small but rapid changes. As before, the large changes occur too slowly to produce any change in state. The small changes occur almost instantly, producing a significant change from one reading to the next, and they do produce changes in the Boolean level.

Practical applications for the dynamic measurement method are few and far between, but do no doubt exist. With a light sensor this mode would ignore slow changes in the ambient light level. It would detect the sudden change in light level caused by the light from a torch, or perhaps the change in level caused by a shadow falling on the sensor. In other words, this mode often allows the ordinary to be ignored, and the unusual to be detected.

BeginOfTask

EndOfTask

Programs downloaded to the RCX unit must be organised into one or more tasks. The BeginOfTask and EndOfTask instructions are used to indicate the beginning and end of each task. Note that these instructions do not actually result in anything being sent to the RCX unit, but they are needed by Spirit.OCX to enable it to correctly organise the data that is downloaded to the RCX unit. These instructions are not required when using the RCX unit in the immediate mode. Note that BeginOfTask is followed by the number of the task (0 to 9), but no number is required in an EndOfTask instruction.

GoSub

BeginOfSub

EndOfSub

A subroutine, or subprogram as it is also known, is a series of commands that are called up by the main program as and where necessary. A subroutine is normally used where the same task must be performed at various places in a program. Rather than repeating the routine at every point in the program where it is needed, it is defined as a subroutine, and then called from the main program at the appropriate places. Once the subroutine has been performed the program goes back and continues where it left off. The subroutine is called using the GoSub command, and this has one parameter, which is the number used to identify the subroutine. Up to eight subroutines can be used, with numbers from 0 to 7. With many programming languages it is possible for one subroutine to call another. Some memory (called the Stack) is used to keep track of the jumps from one subroutine to another, so that the program can always go back to the right place once a subroutine has been completed. The RCX unit does not have a Stack though, and calling one subroutine from another is not allowed. The subroutine starts with a BeginOfSub instruction and finishes with an EndOfSub type. The BeginOfSub instruction has one parameter, which is the identification number of the routine. The EndOfSub command has no parameters. In this example subroutine 5 is called, and simply switches output C on and off:

```
Spirit1.GoSub 5

...

...

Spirit1.BeginOfSub 5
Spirit1.On "2"
Spirit1.Off "2"
Spirit1.EndOfSub
```

On the face of it there is little difference between a subroutine and a task. The all-important difference is that tasks provide multitasking. In other words, if you call up three tasks one after the other, they will all be performed at once. If three subroutines are called up in the same way, one routine will be completed before the next one is commenced. Tasks are used where you need things to happen simultaneously, such as having two or three sensors continuously monitored. Subroutines are used where you simply wish to use the same routine at various points in a program.

StopTask

StartTask

As their names suggest, these two commands can be used to stop and start a task. These commands carry only one parameter, which is the number of the task to be halted or started.

Timers

The RCX unit has four timers that have 100 millisecond (0.1 second) resolution. There is only one command that controls the timers, and this is the ClearTimer command. This simply resets the specified timer to zero, and after being reset it immediately resumes counting. The timers are numbered from 0 to 3. The timers can be read by certain commands if a value of 1 is used as the type of source parameter. For example, this command would set variable 10 at the value read from timer 2:

```
Spirit1.SetVar 10, 1, 2
```

The While and If commands can also be used to read the timers. This example will keep outputs A and C switched on for ten seconds:

```
Spirit1.ClearTimer 0
Spirit1.While 1, 0, 1, 2, 100
Spirit1.On "02"
Spirit1.EndWhile
Spirit1.Off "02"
```

First Timer 0 is cleared, and then a While loop keeps turning on outputs A and C until the value in Timer 0 reaches 100. Once outputs A and C are switched on, further On instructions obviously have no effect, but they do no harm either. These are the functions of the five parameters in the While loop:

1   While Timer…

0   0

1   is less than…

2   the constant value…

100   100, do this…

The timers have a resolution of 0.1 seconds, so waiting for the count to reach 100 gives the required 10 second delay before the final line switches off the motors.

PlayTone

When you start using the RCX unit you soon become aware that it has a simple sound generator facility that can generate tones. You can utilize this facility via the PlayTone instruction, which has two parameters. The first is the required frequency in hertz, and the second is the duration of the tone in hundredths of a second. The frequency value must be in the range 1 to 20000, which gives coverage of more than the full audio range. The time value must be from 1 to 255. This command would therefore produce a note a 440Hz for two seconds:

```
Spirit1.PlayTone 440, 200
```

If a program includes a list of notes, the list is stored in the RCX unit so that one note is completed before the next one is commenced. It is therefore possible to use this instruction to play simple tunes. Page 110 of the Software Developer Kit includes a chart that shows the frequencies required for a wide range of musical notes, and this is also shown on page 24 of the User Guide provided with the Robotics Invention System.

PlaySystemSound

In addition to simple tones, six predefined sounds can be produced using the PlaySystemSound command. This instruction has a single parameter, which is the number of the sound to be played (0 to 5). These are the available sounds:

Number	Sound
0	Key click
1	Beep…beep
2	Sweep upward in frequency
3	Sweep downward in frequency

Number	Sound
4	Buzzing sound
5	Rapid upward sweep in frequency

This command will provide the buzzing sound, which lasts a second or two:

```
Spirit1.PlaySystemSound 4
```

SetWatch

The RCX unit includes a 24-hour clock facility, or a "software watch" in Lego terminology. The watch can be set to the correct time using the SetWatch command, which is followed by two parameters. These set the hours and the minutes. This command would therefore set the watch to 15:22:

```
Spirit1.SetWatch 15, 22
```

The watch can be read using SetVar, If, and While instructions, and its source number is 14.

InitComm

CloseComm

The InitComm command has to be issued in order to initiate communications with the RCX unit. This command does not send any data to the RCX unit, but instead sets up the appropriate serial port to operate properly with the infrared transmitter. Once communications have been completed, the CloseComm command can be used to restore things to normal operation. It is not essential to use the CloseComm command if the serial port is only used with the infrared transmitter, but it must be used before switching back to use the port with another device.

On the face of it there is no problem in simply adding the CloseComm command at the end of the program used to download software to the RCX unit. In practice this does not work because the CloseComm instruction comes into effect before the software has been fully downloaded. A serial port is relatively slow, so a PC uses a small amount of memory, called a buffer, to store serial port data until it can be transmitted. Presumably the program data is stored in the buffer and then the CloseComm command closes down the infrared transmitter before all the data has been sent.

A delay could be added ahead of the CloseComm command, but there is no way of knowing how long each program will take to transmit. However, this method should work provided you are fairly generous with the amount of time allowed. A simple alternative is to have an extra control button, which issues a CloseComm command and then closes the program used to download the software. The light in the infrared transmitter switches off once the software has been downloaded, so you just wait for this light to go out and then operate the extra button to close communications and terminate the program.

SendPBMessage

This command is used to send data from the RCX unit via the infrared link. This normally means sending data to the PC, but it is possible to have two RCX units communicate via the infrared link. This command can also be used to simply produce a brief burst of infrared "light" from the transmitter. This instruction is followed by two parameters, which are the type of source, and then the exact source. This command will transmit a value of 127

```
Spirit1.SendPBMessage 2, 127
```

Values for transmission must be integers in the range 0 to 255. Incidentally, the PB part of this command's name simply stands for Programmable Brick. This is a term that is often encountered when dealing with Lego MindStorms kits, and it is just another name for the RCX unit.

Sources

As we have already seen, several commands use parameters that are given via an indirect means, with the first parameter giving the type of source (constant, variable, etc.), and the second pointing to the source more precisely (the actual value of a constant, the number of a variable, etc.). This is a full list of the available sources, but note that not all of these sources are usable with some commands. The charts in the Software Developer Kit show the sources that are applicable to each command.

Number	Source	Second parameter
0	Variable	Number of variable (0 - 31)
1	Timer	Number of timer (0 - 3)
2	Constant	Value to be used (−32768 to +32767)
3	Motor status	Motor number (0, 1, or 2)
4	Random	Maximum value for number (1 - 32767)
5	Tacho counter	Counter number (0 or 1)
6	Tacho speed	Speed number (0 or 1)
7	Motor current	2
8	Program number	0
9	Sensor reading	Number of sensor (0, 1, or 2)
10	Sensor type	Number of sensor (0, 1, or 2)
11	Sensor mode	Number of sensor (0, 1, or 2)
12	Sensor raw	Number of sensor (0, 1, or 2)
13	Sensor Boolean	Number of sensor (0, 1, or 2)
14	Watch	0
15	PB Message	0
16	AGC	0

Some of these are the type of thing that you will need to use time and time again, such as constants and variables, while others have to be regarded as non-essential. Note that sources 5, 6, 7, and 16 only apply to the Lego CyberMaster kits, and not those that utilize an RCX unit.

The commands described here are the main ones that are needed for general programming. There are some others detailed in the Software developer Kit, but they are mostly only applicable to the Lego CyberMaster kits.

Number confusion

When programming the RCX unit using Spirit.OCX there is potential confusion over the numbering of the input ports, timers, etc. It stems from a common problem in computing, which is that most people expect numbering to start at 1, but computers number everything from zero. Hence the inputs of the RCX unit are labelled "1", "2", and "3", but in programs that utilize Spirit.OCX they are referred to as inputs "0", "1", and "2" respectively. Things go further awry with the outputs, which are named "A", "B", and "C", presumably to avoid confusion with the inputs. In programs that use Spirit.OCX they are referred to as output "0", "1", and "2" respectively.

Most programming languages provide a way around this in the form of variables. For example, you could assign a value of 0 to a variable named "Output-A" and a value of 2 to a variable called "Constant". The variables can then be used in the program, as in these example instructions:

```
Spirit1.On "Output-A"
Wait Constant, 50
```

In the first example the programming language will substitute a value of 0 for the variable, and output A will be switched on. In the second instruction the programming language substitutes a value of 2 for the variable, which sets the source of delay value as a constant. This constant is, of course, the value of 50 given in the second parameter of the instruction.

With this system you can avoid any confusing numbering systems, and also replace code numbers with something less cryptic, as in the second example. One problem with this system is that a large number of variables are required in order to tackle all the numbering adjustments and code numbers. Many Lego MindStorms programs are very short, and it could reasonably be deemed a bit "over the top" to bother with the redefining process. Another point to bear in mind is that having assigned values to the variables you must be careful to get their names absolutely spot-on in your programs. If you declare a variable as "Output-1" it is no good referring to it as "Output1" or "Output_1" in your program code. The programming language will not know what you mean and with produce an error message.

The example programs in this book use raw code with no redefining via variables. A list of suggested variables and values for them is provided in the Software Developer Kit (SDK), and it is worthwhile consulting this if you are interested in using this method. Of course, you can use your own variable names if preferred, but make sure that you keep within the rules for variable names. Most modern programming languages are easy-going about variable names, but none give the programmer totally free rein.

Using Visual BASIC

Visual BASIC 6

In the space available here it is not possible to give details of using Spirit.OCX with a wide range of programming languages. We will concentrate on Visual BASIC 6, which is the obvious choice as it is by far the most popular programming language. The examples given here should also work with Visual BASIC 5, but note that this version has somewhat different menu structures to version 6. If you try these examples using Visual BASIC 5 it might be necessary to search through the menus to find some of menu items mentioned here. There are five versions of Visual BASIC 6, and any of them should be suitable for writing control programs for Lego robots. The three commercial flavours are the Standard version, the more expensive Professional Edition, and the even more costly Enterprise Edition. There is also an Academic version, but this is more or less the Professional Edition with different licensing conditions.

There is also a "free" version that is very occasionally given away on the cover discs of computer magazines, and it is also supplied with some beginners' books about programming Visual BASIC. This is virtually the full program, and it has full save facilities, etc., and can run any programs you write with it or load into it. Its main limitations are the lack of any online help and an inability to compile a standalone program file or a program group that can be installed on a PC. Programs can only be run from within Visual BASIC 6, rather like running programs using a BASIC interpreter such as GW BASIC or QBASIC. This is not necessarily a major drawback in the current context, where you will probably not wish to compile and install lots of small programs on your PC anyway. It is probably best to run them from within Visual BASIC 6, which avoids having to compile and install numerous programs, and also makes it easy to implement changes to the programs. You only need to compile programs if they are to be distributed to people who do not have Visual BASIC 6. Bear in mind though, that the compiled program can only be used as is, and that even the most minor changes to the code are not possible.

VBA

It is perhaps worth mentioning VBA here, which is Visual BASIC for Applications. This is a program that is supplied with a number of Microsoft applications programs, including Word and some of the other Microsoft Office programs. It is also supplied with some other Windows programs, such as AutoCAD 2000. Although I have sometimes seen it suggested that there is no difference between Visual BASIC and VBA, this is far from the truth. The two programs have different purposes, and Visual BASIC is, of course, primarily intended for producing standalone programs.

VBA on the other hand, is designed for adding new features to existing applications. This does not mean that VBA can not be used with Spirit.OCX to download programs to the RCX unit, etc., and it is indeed possible to use VBA in this fashion. It does mean that VBA can not be used in exactly the same way as Visual BASIC. VBA would not be my first choice for use with the Robotics Invention System, but if you have this on your computer but do not have Visual BASIC, it is certainly worthwhile giving it a try.

Starting with VB

When Visual BASIC is first run you are presented with a window that offers various program types (Figure 2.1), but for our purposes the default Standard.EXE option will suffice. Simply press the Open button to select this. Once into Visual BASIC you will see several windows open on the screen, which should look something like Figure 2.2. The window covered with a

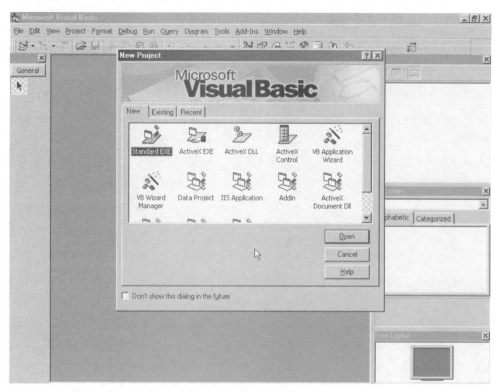

Fig.2.1 The initial screen when Visual BASIC 6 is run

grid of dots and called Form1 is the one that you use to design the window in which the compiled program will run. The compiled program will run in a window the same size as the form. If a control button is place on the form an identical button will appear at the same position when the program is run. In this case the programs may never be compiled and installed as standalone programs, and may simply be run from within Visual BASIC. However, when the program is run a new window containing the control buttons, etc., will appear.

The form is contained in a window called Form1 (Form). There is another window hidden behind this one, and double clicking on the form will bring the hidden window to the front (Figure 2.3). This window is called Form1 (Code), and it is where the BASIC program code is entered. There are two lines of code already present and any instructions that must be carried out when the

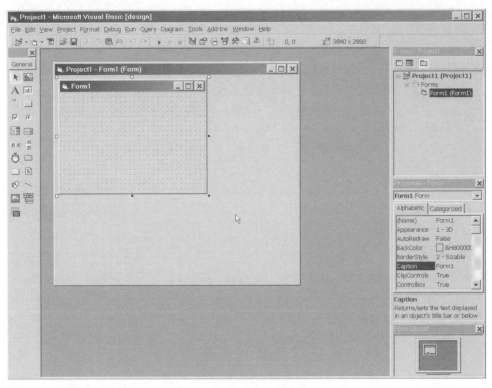

Fig.2.2 The screen obtained once Visual BASIC is up and running

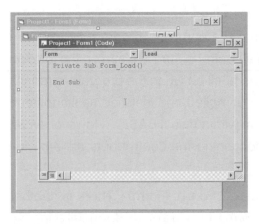

Fig.2.3 The Code window

program is launched are added between these two lines. If buttons and other objects are added to the form, the basic code for these will be automatically added to the code window. Down the left-hand side of the screen there are various objects that can be added to the form, and this part of the screen is called the Toolbox. The purpose of many of the objects in the Toolbox is readily apparent from the icons used.

However, placing the cursor over any of the icons will bring up a brief description of its function.

Command buttons

The component we will need most is the Command Button object. If it is not already fully visible left-click anywhere on the form to bring it to the fore. Then left-click on the Command Button icon and place the cursor over the form. Left-click on the form and then drag a rectangle of suitable size for the control button. Once the button has been created it can be dragged to any required point on the screen, and it has eight handles that permit it to be easily resized.

The button will be labelled Command1 by default, but it is easily relabelled. In the right-hand section of the screen there is a Properties window, and this shows the current properties of the selected object. Left-clicking on the form or an object on the form will make it the current item and bring up its details in the Properties window, but the new button will already be the current object. If you look in the Properties window you will find a property called Caption, and beside this it will say Command1. In order to edit this name left-click on Command1 and then change it to whatever you require using normal text editing methods. In this case the caption is changed to DOWNLOAD, which should immediately result in the label on the button changing in sympathy.

You can also change the name of a command button or any other component. Note that changing the caption does not automatically change the name of a component as well, and that the caption and component name can be different. With a form that contains very few components it is far from essential to bother about renaming. With only one or two buttons you are unlikely to get confused and assign program code to the wrong one. When there are numerous components to deal with, and particularly if there are several components of the same type, renaming each component with a more meaningful name is definitely a good idea. The name is always at the top in the Properties window, and it can be edited just like any other property. Having changed the name, that name must be used in any program code that refers to the component or one of its properties. Renaming components is optional, but the form is invariably renamed to something more appropriate, and then the form and its contents are saved to disc under this name.

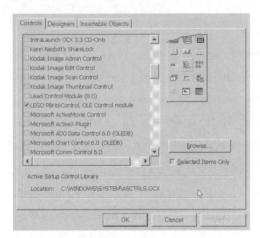

Fig.2.4 Spirit.OCX should appear in the list of components

Loading Spirit.OCX

As explained in chapter 1, in order to write code that can be sent to the RCX unit the Spirit.OCX control is required. This object is loaded onto the form in exactly the same way as command buttons and other objects. There is a slight problem though, and if you look at the objects in the window down the left-hand side of the screen it is unlikely that Spirit.OCX will actually be there. It will probably not be loaded by default, and you must add it manually. To do this, activate the Project menu and then select Components. This brings up a list of additional objects, and in the alphabetical list you should find one having a name that starts with the word Lego. It will probably be called something like PBrick Control rather than Spirit, but this is the component you require. Left-click on the box beside its entry to place a tick there (Figure 2.4), and then operate the Apply and OK buttons. The very distinctive Lego logo should then appear in the palette of objects.

If for some reason Spirit.OCX is not in the list of objects you must select the Browse option and then find it. By default it will be placed in the C:\Program Files\LEGO MINDSTORMS\System directory. It is assumed here that the Lego software has been installed on drive C, and the path must be changed accordingly if it has been installed on another drive. Having found Spirit.OCX using the file browser, left-click on its entry to select it and then operate the Open button to add it to the list. It can then be added into the palette of objects in the usual way.

It should not be necessary to go through this procedure each time Visual BASIC is run, and having loaded Spirit.OCX once it should be automatically loaded each time Visual BASIC is launched. Unfortunately, things can sometimes go slightly awry, and this mainly seems to happen when the PC has one or more versions of VBA installed in addition to Visual BASIC. The new control usually loads into VBA correctly, but unfortunately it has to be added to Visual BASIC each time it is run. If there is an easy solution to this problem I am unaware of it. You simply have to keep loading the control, or save a form with this control added and use it as your starting point.

Visibility

As explained previously, Spirit.OCX is added onto the form like any other component, but there is an obvious difference in that it does not actually interact directly with the user when the program is running. You can not left-click on it to make something happen, and it does not display any information using text or graphics. Spirit.OCX must still be added to the form so that its additional facilities can be used, but it is advisable to make its icon as small as possible.

The icon can be visible or hidden when a program is run. With this type of thing it is normal for it to be hidden, since there is otherwise a risk of users thinking that it's a command button and that left-clicking on it should make something happen. In order to hide the icon, first select Spirit.OCX and then look at its properties in the Properties window. Select the Visible property, left-click on the button that appears to its right, and then select False. Note that the icon will still be visible on the form, but it will not appear on the screen when the program is run.

Adding code

So far we have a Visual BASIC form with Spirit.OCX added, together with a control button (Figure 2.5), but the button does not actually do anything. Double clicking on the control button will bring up the Code window, and the cursor will be placed between the two lines of code for the button that has been added for you by Visual BASIC. The code for the control button must be placed between the two existing lines of code.

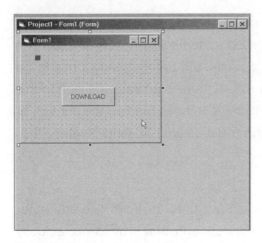

Fig.2.5 The form, complete with command button

Notice that the first line of code ends with Click(). This means that the code you enter will be performed when the control button is left-clicked. There are other options available, but you will normally require the code for a button to be performed only when the button is left-clicked. This is certainly all we require here, so there is no need to alter the default setting, but this is easily done via the Properties window for the button.

This simple test program will enable you to check that everything is working correctly, in addition to illustrating some fundamental points. It simply switches on the motors connected to outputs A and C, waits two seconds, and then switches the motors off again. Add the extra lines of code so that the complete routine for the control button looks like this:

```
Private Sub Command1_Click()

Spirit1.InitComm

Spirit1.SelectPrgm 1

Spirit1.BeginOfTask 0

Spirit1.On "02"

Spirit1.Wait 2, 200

Spirit1.Off "02"

Spirit1.EndOfTask

End Sub
```

Even the least observant will have noticed that each of the new lines starts with Spirit1., and this is because the code in all these lines relies on Spirit.OCX. There are no lines in pure Visual BASIC. The name of the ActiveX control is added ahead of each command, with a full stop between the two so that Visual BASIC can be sure which part is the name of the control and which is the command. Having the name of the ActiveX control added ahead of a command tells Visual BASIC that the command is not part of its normal repertoire, and that it needs the additional facilities of the ActiveX control.

Note that the name of the control is Spirit1, and not just Spirit. When an object is added to a form a number is always added after its name. The button added to the form was called Command1, and if further buttons were added they would be Command2, Command3, etc. As already pointed out, it is possible to edit the name of an object via the Properties window. Although some people prefer to change Spirit to something more apposite, it is probably best not confuse matters and to simply leave the control's name as Spirit1. All the examples in this book assume that the name is left unaltered, and they will have to be changed accordingly if a different name is used.

The first of the new lines simply initialises the infrared link to the RCX unit. This does not actually result in anything being sent to the RCX unit, and its purpose is to get the PC ready to use the infrared link. The next line specifies a program number, which is actually a block of memory in the RCX unit that is reserved for program storage. There are five of these memory blocks and five program numbers available.

On the RCX unit's display these are numbered from 1 to 5, but in programs you must use numbers from 0 to 4. As pointed out at the end of chapter 1, this anomaly crops up quite frequently when writing programs for the RCX unit, and is not uncommon in general computing. It is not that difficult to remember that an adjustment of one is needed in some values, but you can adopt the use of variables to smooth things out if you keep making mistakes. In this case we are using program number 1, which is program 2 as far as the RCX unit's display is concerned.

Tasks

Line three of the additional code starts a task, and in this case it is the only task. There can be up to ten tasks numbered from 0 to 9, and they can run simultaneously if necessary. For example, there could be two touch sensors and a light type, with a separate task continuously monitoring each one. This type of thing is normally organised on the basis of a main task which does any initial setting up that is required and then starts the other tasks. Where this multitasking is not required, there must still be one task, because the RCX unit only understands programs that are organised as one or more tasks. Hence our simple motor control example is the main task, and does not call any additional tasks.

If no tasks are used, the RCX unit will assume that you are using direct mode, and the instructions will be performed immediately. At least, those that are available in direct mode will be performed at once. Any others will simply be ignored.

Having indicated the beginning of a task, the next lines actually make that task do something. In this case the motors on outputs 0 and 2 are switched on. The outputs of the RCX unit are marked A, B, and C, but when using Spirit.OCX they are referred to as outputs 0, 1, and 2 respectively. A Wait instruction then results in the program doing nothing for two seconds. The first figure in this instruction (2) indicates that the source of the delay is a constant, which means the delay is controlled by the second figure in the instruction (200). The delay is set with a resolution of 10 milliseconds, or in one hundredths of a second if you prefer. A value of 200 therefore provides a delay of two seconds.

An Off instruction then switches off both motors. Finally, an EndOfTask instruction tells the RCX unit that the end of the program has been reached. You must be careful to include this instruction at the end of each task, because programs will certainly fail to operate properly if they are omitted.

In order to try this program, activate the Run menu and then select Start. The program should then run, and it should look like the form but without the grid of dots (Figure 2.6). Set up the infrared transmitter in exactly the same way as you do when transferring RCX code to the RCX unit, and then operate the DOWNLOAD button. This should result in the green light in the transmitter switching on for a few seconds while the program is transferred to the RCX unit. The program number that appears on the RCX unit's display should be 2, together with four zeros on the left-hand section of the display.

Fig.2.6 The window produced when the program is run

If all is well, pressing the Run button on the RCX unit will result in the motors running forwards for two seconds. If not, carefully check through the program for errors and then try again. With programs it helps to bear in mind that if you get everything right it will work. If you do not get everything just right, then a program will certainly not work. To terminate the Visual BASIC program left-click on the cross in the top right-hand corner of the program window.

VB shortcut

Putting Spirit1 ahead of every command that utilises Spirit.OCX can be a bit tedious even when entering short programs into Visual BASIC. With longer programs it can become very irksome indeed. Fortunately, Visual BASIC provides a shortcut in the form of its With facility. Simply add With Spirit1 ahead of a block of instructions that use Spirit.OCX, and End With after the last of these instructions. The Spirit1 prefix can then be omitted from each instruction. Using the method the test program provided earlier can be reduced to this:

```
Private Sub Command1_Click()

With Spirit1

.InitComm

.SelectPrgm 1
```

```
.BeginOfTask 0

.On "02"

.Wait 2, 200

.Off "02"

.EndOfTask

End With

End Sub
```

VB alternatives

If you do not have access to Visual BASIC there are alternative means of downloading your programs to the RCX unit, and a tour of Lego MindStorms related web sites will soon find a few of these alternatives. There are complete programming languages such a NQC (not quite C), and software that enables Visual BASIC style programs to be downloaded to the RCX unit. In order to download the programs featured in this book it is clearly one of these Visual BASIC alternatives that is required. Probably the best known of these, and the only one I have tried, is BrickCommand (Figure 2.7) which is at version 2.0 at the time of writing this. This program is freeware, so there is no charge for using it.

One or two points have to be borne in mind when using BrickCommand with programs written for Visual BASIC. The first of these is that it is only suitable for programs that are downloaded to the RCX unit and then run within the RCX unit. It is not suitable for Visual BASIC programs that control the robot in immediate mode. This is due to the fact that BrickCommand does not have the range of Visual BASIC instructions, controls, graphics, and other features that are used with this type of program. It is designed for downloading software to the RCX unit, which it does very well.

BrickCommand does have an immediate mode that provides a sort of remote control facility that is usable with many robots (Figure 2.8). Obviously a general

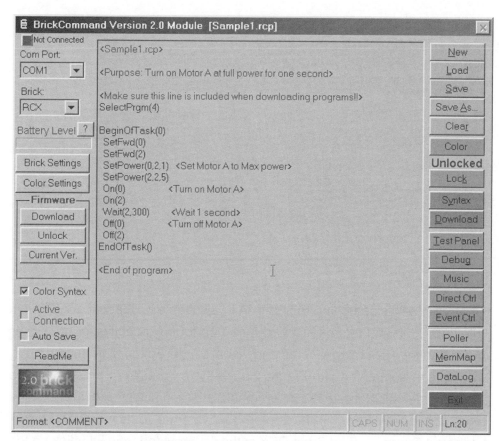

Fig.2.7 The BrickCommand program in operation

purpose program of this type is more apposite to some robots than it is to others, but it is often useful for testing robots in direct mode.

When using BrickCommand there is no need to use InitComm and CloseComm, as the program handles all this for you. Neither is it necessary to put Spirit1. at the beginning of every command, because the program knows that all the commands require Spirit.OCX. Parameters are placed within parentheses, with no space between the command word and the first parenthesis. The parentheses are still needed even if an instruction does not have any parameters. The simple test program provided earlier in this chapter would therefore be reduced to this if used with BrickCommand:

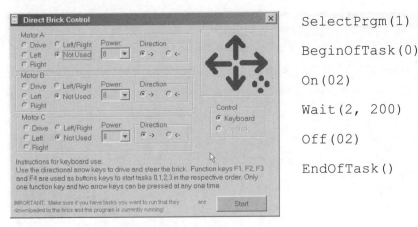

SelectPrgm(1)

BeginOfTask(0)

On(02)

Wait(2, 200)

Off(02)

EndOfTask()

Fig.2.8 The remote control program

Using VBA

It may take a little searching to find VBA in a suitable host application, but in AutoCAD 2000 and Microsoft Word it can be found by activating the Tools menu, and then selecting Macros and Visual BASIC Editor. This should bring up a screen something like Figure 2.9. If there is no form present on the screen by default, activate the Insert menu and then select User Form. If the Lego logo is not present in the Toolbox, activate the Tools menu and select Additional Controls. Find Spirit.OCX in the list provided, and left-click on the box beside its entry in order to add it to the Toolbox. It appears as Spirit Control on my PC, but it might be listed under a different name. Operate the OK button to go back to the VBA editor, and the icon for Spirit.OCX should then appear in the Toolbox. Remember that you must add the Spirit.OCX control to the form, and that it is not enough to simply have it present in the Toolbox.

Things are then much as before, with a button being added to the form, along with the Spirit.OCX control. Double-click on the button to bring up the Code window so that the program for the button can be added. When the program has been entered, activate the Run menu and select Run Sub/User Form to test it. The program window will then appear, and activating the button will download the program to the RCX unit. A Properties window for the form will

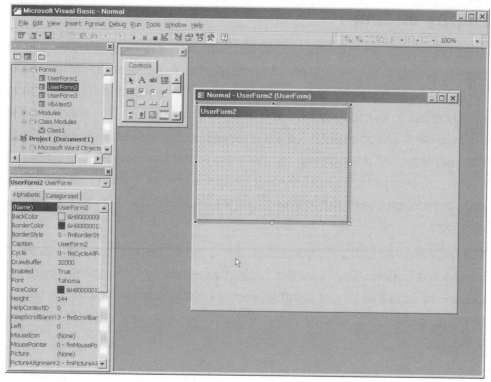

Fig.2.9 The opening screen of VBA

appear if you click on the form to make it active. You can then change its name and caption to something more suitable, and save the form, either by operating the appropriate button or via the File menu. The new form will then be added to the list in the window towards the top left-hand corner of the screen. A form is closed by left-clicking on the cross in the top right-hand corner of its window, and retrieved by double-clicking on its entry in the list of forms.

Using VBA is admittedly rather more limited than programming with the "real thing", but it can certainly be used to try out some programs, and at zero cost if you already have an application that includes VBA.

Happy ending

If we return now to our simple test program, one obvious refinement is to provide it with a proper means of ending once the downloading has been completed. As it stands, the program can only be terminated by left-clicking on the cross in the top right-hand corner of the window. This winds up the program well enough, but it leaves a serial port set for use with the infrared communicator. If the port will not be used with other devices this does not matter too much, but it is very easy to add a control button that will close communications with the infrared communicator and then terminate the program.

First add another button to the screen using the same method that was used for the first button. Then use the Properties window to change the button's caption to something more suitable, such as END. Double-click on the button to bring up the Code window, and then edit the code for the button so that it looks like this:

```
Private Sub Command2_Click()

Spirit1.CloseComm

End

End Sub
```

The first of the two additional lines closes communication with the infrared link, and the second of the new lines ends the program. The program is used in much the same way as the original, with the DOWNLOAD button being used to start downloading the program once everything has been switched on and set up correctly. The END button is operated once the light in the infrared tower has switched off and communication with the RCX unit has ceased. Figure 2.10 shows the window produced when the program is run.

Demo program

Subsequent chapters in this book provide numerous examples of practical programs that utilize Spirit.OCX, so there is no point in providing masses of demonstration programs here. We will settle for one more example program that demonstrates simple program flow and monitoring a sensor. This program requires a form equipped with Spirit.OCX, and two command

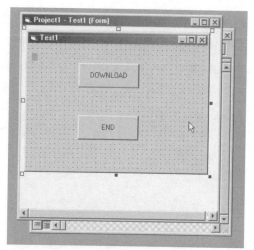

Fig.2.10 The additional button on the form

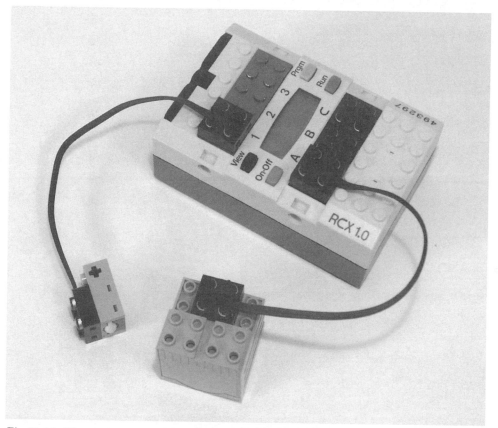

Fig.2.11 The set-up used to test the demo program

buttons labelled DOWNLOAD and END. These buttons are Command1 and Command2 respectively. A motor is connected to output A of the RCX unit, and a touch switch is connected to input 1. This simple test set-up is shown in Figure 2.11.

```
Private Sub Command1_Click()

With Spirit1

.InitComm

.SelectPrgm 2

.BeginOfTask 0

.On "0"

.SetSensorType 0, 1

.Loop 2, 0

.If 9, 0, 2, 2, 1

.SetRwd "0"

.Else

.SetFwd "0"

.EndIf

.EndLoop

.EndOfTask

End With

End Sub


Private Sub Command2_Click()

Spirit1.CloseComm

End

End Sub
```

The program starts by opening communication with the infrared link and selecting program 2, which is program number 3 in the RCX unit's numbering system. The first and only task then starts, and the first instruction switches on the motor connected to output 0, which is the output marked as A on the RCX unit. The sensor type for input 0 is then set. Of course, input 0 is the input port labelled 1 on the RCX unit. The code number for the sensor type is 1, which means that this input is set to operate with a switch (touch) sensor. No SetSensorMode instruction is used, and we are simply settling for the default mode used for a switch sensor. This is the Boolean mode, which means that the input value will be either 0 when the switch is not activated or 1 when it is.

Next the program goes into the main routine, which is an indefinite loop. The loop is made to operate indefinitely by using a value of zero for the number of times that the loop must be performed. The loop causes an If...Then...Else structure to be performed over and over again. All this routine does is to repeatedly check the setting of the touch switch. The motor is set for forward operation if the switch is not operated, or to go backwards if the sensor is operated. The five parameters in the If instruction break down like this:

9   Read sensor number...

0   0

2   If the sensor value equals...

2   The constant value...

1   1, then do this...

A value of 1 is read from the sensor when it is activated, and the following instruction is then performed. This sets the motor to go in reverse. A value of 0 is read if the sensor is not activated, and the instruction after the Else command is then performed. This sets the motor to go forward. The next three instructions end the If...Then...Else structure, the loop, and the task. You have to be careful to close loops, tasks, etc., and an error message will be produced when the program is run if this is not done properly. It is also essential to terminate things in the right order. This will usually be the opposite of the order in which they were created, as in this case. Finally, the use of the With facility is closed, and the simple routine for the END button is included right at the end of the listing.

If you try this program the motor should run as soon as the program is started. Operating the touch switch should reverse the direction of the motor, and releasing the switch should return it to forward operation again. If you press the RCX unit's View button once, the display with show the sensor value. This should be 0 under standby conditions and 1 when the switch is operated. The View facility is very useful when dealing with sensors, and this facility should always be used to check readings when sensors do not seem to be giving the right results.

Making Connections

Right connections

Lego produce a varied and useful selection of sensors for the MindStorms kits, including touch, light, temperature, and rotation sensors. However, building your own sensors can extend the range of possibilities still further. Before you can make your own sensors the problem of connecting the sensors to the RCX unit has to be overcome. The easy way of doing things is to use a standard Lego lead. Four short leads and two long types are included as standard in the Robotics Invention System. I would certainly not recommend chopping up any of the short leads for use with your own sensors, because these leads are required for the two motors and two touch sensors included in the kit.

If you can obtain some extra leads, it is all right to go ahead and adapt them for use with do-it-yourself sensors. However, if you cut one of these leads in half to produce two leads for you own sensors, the cable on each connector will only be about 63 millimetres long, or should that be 63 millimetres short? Both cables will be too short to be of any practical value. Obviously extension leads can be added, or you can cut off and discard one connector so that the other connector is left with a full-length lead. This second method is clearly rather wasteful, but it is the easier option.

If you add extension leads make sure that the soldered connections are well insulated so that there is no danger of short circuits occurring. Instead of soldering extension leads onto the cables you can use small connector blocks,

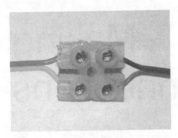

Fig.3.1 *Two leads joined via a connector block*

which are available from many do-it-yourself superstores as well as electronic component retailers. These blocks are usually sold in strips of 10 or 12 connectors, but they are easily cut down to the required size using a sharp modelling knife. They are also available with various current ratings, but for our purposes the smallest type you can obtain should be more than adequate. They have screw terminals that eliminate the need for any soldering, and the heavy insulation around each terminal rules out any accidental short circuits. Figure 3.1 shows a terminal block used to join two twin leads.

The Robotics Invention System includes two longer connecting leads that are around 1.25 metres in length. These are little used, and unless you have a definite need for both of them it makes sense to modify one of them for use

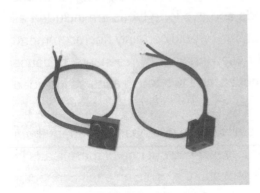

Fig.3.2 *Two leads for use with DIY sensors*

with do-it-yourself sensors. Simply cutting one of these leads in half will provide two leads that are over 600 millimetres long. This is excessive for normal requirements, so it is a good idea to cut the cable to leave leads about 150 to 200 millimetres long attached to each connector. The twin cable should be split at the end so that a few millimetres of insulation can be stripped from each lead. This cable seems to be tougher than most, and a pair of small but sharp scissors will be needed to separate the two leads. Ideally the bare ends of the leads should be tinned with solder. Two leads cut from a long connecting cable are shown in Figure 3.2.

Note that extra Lego leads of various lengths are available, and that you can buy some of these if you wish to make some leads for use with your own sensors, but would prefer to leave the Robotics Invention System intact. This is certainly the method that I would recommend. This method costs a few pounds, but the capabilities of the basic kit are not impaired in any way. Also, if you start chopping up leads from the kit you will almost certainly invalidate the guarantee. If you require more than two connectors the only safe option is to buy some extra leads. If you chop up more than one lead from the kit you will probably soon regret it, and end up buying replacements for the cannibalised leads.

DIY connectors

The alternative to adapting Lego leads, and probably the more popular approach to making connections to the RCX unit, is to convert some standard Lego bricks into Lego style connectors. Depending on the type of connector you make, these will permit connections to be made to the RCX unit either via the leads supplied with the kit, or direct to the RCX unit. If you make your sensors like the Lego touch sensors, with terminals on the top, the sensor can be connected to the RCX unit by way of standard Lego leads. Alternatively, you can make female connectors, like those on the Lego leads. These will connect direct to the input and output ports of the RCX unit.

It is possible to buy a Lego Basic kit for a few pounds if you do not wish to sacrifice any of the bricks in the Robotics Invention System. One of these kits provides dozens of bricks of various sizes, so it will not matter too much if you write-off a few bricks in the process of making some connectors that are just right. There is a big advantage in buying some extra bricks to use as the basis for connectors. The Robotics Invention System includes a substantial number of ordinary bricks, but if you start using these for connectors it is possible that you will get "caught short" when building some robots. Buying a Lego Basic kit costs very little, and actually gives you more parts for building robots since there is little chance of using all the bricks for connectors. I would certainly recommend this way of handling do-it-yourself connectors. Again, if you start modifying bricks from the Robotics Invention System it is likely that the guarantee will be invalidated.

Simple approach

The simplest method of converting bricks into connectors is to use small cheese head screws. The head needs to be 3/16 inches in diameter, which equates to 4.76 millimetres. Apparently MindStorms enthusiasts living in the USA generally use 4/40 machine screws. I found quarter inch (6.35 millimetre) 6BA screws to be the best choice for UK users, but the old imperial measures are, of course, being phased out in favour of metric sizes. Metric M2.5 screws seem to be fractionally too small, and M3 screws are fractionally too large but usable provided they do not put too much strain on the connector fitted to them.

Fig.3.3 Stage one of construction completed

The first step is to drill a hole about 2.5 millimetres in diameter in two of the spigots at the top of a brick. The easiest way of doing this is to drill the holes from the underside. If you look into the underside of a Lego brick you will see that there are "dimples" under each of the spigots, and these act as guides which virtually guarantee that the holes will be drilled accurately. Having drilled the two holes you should have something like Figure 3.3.

Fig.3.4 Next two spigots are removed

Next the two lumps in which the holes have been drilled must be removed. If you have one of those little multi-purpose power tools and a suitable cutting blade, this should slice them straight off and make a very neat job. If not, a handheld twist drill bit of about 5 millimetres can be used to initially cut away the spigots. It is best to finish off using a larger bit of around nine or 10 millimetres in diameter. This will completely remove the spigots without cutting too deeply into the top of the brick. Alternatively, file away the two spigots using a small flat file. The bricks are made from quite soft plastic, but this could still be quite time consuming. With the spigots removed you should have something like Figure 3.4.

Ideally self-tapping screws would now be fitted into the holes, but self-tapping screws having the required size and head type are unlikely to be available. This leaves two options, one of which is to use ordinary screws as if they were of the self-tapping variety. The 2.5 millimetre holes in the brick are slightly undersize for 6BA screws, and the bricks are made from quite soft plastic. With a little gentle persuasion the screws can be fitted into the holes much as if they were the self-tapping variety. If the screws can not be fitted into the holes, try fractionally enlarging the holes using a miniature round file. If you try this method be careful not to over-tighten the screws. Attempting to do them up really tightly will simply

Fig.3.5 The two bolts
in place

shear the threads pressed into the plastic, leaving the screws quite loose. A small amount of super glue applied around the holes is a better way of persuading the screws to stay in place. This gives a finished assembly like Figure 3.5.

The problem with this method is that the screws are not fitted in place really securely. The obvious alternative is to drill out the holes to about three millimetres in diameter, and then use fixing nuts to hold the bolts securely in place. However, this is not quite as simple as it might seem. There is only a very limited amount of space inside a Lego brick, and there is not enough space for some of the more generously proportioned 6BA nuts. The

Fig.3.6 The nut fitted onto
the bolt

smaller ones will just about fit, but it is very difficult to get them down into place so that they can be fitted to the screws. They tend to flip over sideways, as they fit into the brick much easier this way round.

Fig.3.7 Both nuts in position

Fig.3.8 The completed connector

The only way around the problem I could find is to first fit a long 6BA bolt into one of the holes and then fit a nut onto this. With the screw to keep the nut the right way up it will then go down into the brick without too much difficulty (Figure 3.6). Keep turning the screw until the nut is fully tightened, and then carefully undo the screw, leaving the nut in place. Repeat this process for the other nut, and you then have something like Figure 3.7. Finally, fit the two 6.35 millimetre bolts (Figure 3.8).

If necessary, the plastic tube in the middle of the brick can be drilled away to provide a bit more space to work with. This will probably make the brick a slightly less secure fit when it is fitted onto another brick, but it should still be a reasonably firm fit.

Checking connections

With the bolts in place it is a good idea to connect your new connector to the RCX unit to check that it does actually work. The View facility of the RCX unit is ideal when testing new connectors and home-made sensors, since it shows exactly what is and what is not happening. The display can be used to show the data returned from any of the three inputs on the RCX unit. With the RCX unit switched on, press the View button once and an arrow mark will appear beneath "1" to indicate that the display is showing the value read from input 1. Further presses of the View button will move the arrowhead so that it appears beneath the "2" and "3" marks above the display, indicating that the data appearing on the display is read from input 2 and 3 respectively. Incidentally, further presses of the view button result in the display showing the status of outputs A, B, and C, and a further press takes things back to normal operation.

The form the data takes depends on the operating mode of the input. This will usually be 0 to 1023 (raw mode), 0 to 100 (percentage mode), or 0 and 1 (Boolean mode). For testing a connector it does not really matter which of these modes is used, since they will all indicate the difference between an open circuit and a short circuit. However, it is not a good idea to try this method of testing with the input set for operation with an active sensor such

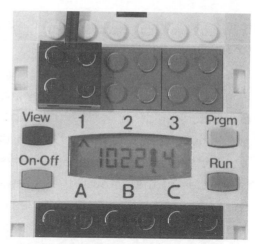

Fig.3.9 *The display under standby conditions*

as a light type. With an active sensor the input also acts as a power source for much of the time. It is best to run a program that uses input 1 with a touch sensor, which is a passive sensor. Input 1 will remain in this mode once the program has been stopped, and it is not necessary to have a program running while using the View facility.

With the new connector wired to input 1, press the View button once to monitor this input and then look for a change in the readings when the bolts are connected together on the underside of the brick. In raw mode for example, the reading should be 1023 or perhaps 1022 (Figure 3.9), changing to a low reading of about one or two when the two screws are short-circuited (Figure 3.10). Touching a screwdriver blade onto both bolts is

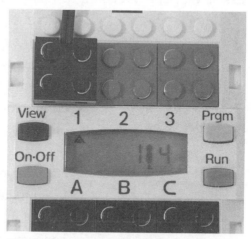

Fig.3.10 *The display reading with the leads short-circuited*

all that is needed to make an electrical connection between them. With the input in Boolean mode, which is the default mode for a touch sensor, the reading is 0 under standby conditions and 1 when the two bolts are short-circuited.

Provided you obtain a change in reading the connector is working properly. If no change is obtained then there is certainly a problem. Most home-made connectors made in the way described previously work first time with no problems. Occasionally one or both of the bolt heads may fail to make contact with the connectors on the leads. This might be due to the manufacturing tolerances of the screws, the screws not being properly centred, or a combination of the two. If a connector fails to work it is probably best to rebuild it using another brick. If the second attempt also fails to work it is likely that the heads of the bolts are just fractionally too small. Bear in mind that if there is a gap of a 10 thousandths of an inch between the head of the screw and the plate in the other connector, no electrical connection will be made. In fact a gap even smaller than this is sufficient to completely "gum up the works".

All is not lost if no change in reading is obtained, and it is possible to retrieve matters if a do-it-yourself connector fails to connect. Clean the heads of the screws with wire wool or by scraping them with the small blade of a penknife.

Fig.3.11 Solder added to the bolts

They should then accept a coating of solder on the outside edges (Figure 3.11), which will effectively enlarge them to the point where contact is made with the plates in the other connector. In fact the amount of solder will probably be slightly overgenerous, and you may have to file some of it away. The connector that fits onto your home-made connector should not look bloated once it is in place. It merely needs to be tight enough to produce a good electrical connection. If there is any excess flux in evidence it should be scraped or cleaned away, since it could otherwise insulate the bolt heads from the plates in the other connector.

One drawback of this method is that it is not very neat. Things have had to be fudged in order obtain successful connections, and that is what it looks like. On the plus side, it seems to work very well. If you can not find suitable screws, it is possible to use some that are known to be too small and then add some solder so that they make the connections.

Making connections

Having checked that the connectors are making good contacts with the Lego leads it is then a matter of making the connections from your sensor circuit to the screws. With a very simple sensor, such as a basic light type, there will only be one component to deal with. This component will be mounted on the brick and then wired direct to the two screws. Figure 3.12 shows a simple light sensor that uses this method. Making the connections to the screws is a bit awkward because they are recessed into the brick, but they are still within the reach of a miniature soldering iron. The solder will take quite well to screws provided they are clean, so scrape the end of each one using a penknife or modelling knife. Tin each screw with solder and

Fig.3.12 A simple light sensor

then tin the ends of both leads with a plentiful supply of solder. The leads should then join to the bolts without any difficulty. Try not to leave large blobs of solder on each joint as this could prevent the brick from fitting onto another brick properly.

With the more complex sensors it is not usually possible to fit everything into a brick, even one of the larger types. It is then necessary to improvise, with the unit being based on something like a large plate or the base section included in a Lego Basic kit. A home-made connector can still be used with this type of sensor, and it is just a matter of drilling a hole in the brick to take a small twin lead that connects to the two bolts (Figure 3.13). The other end of the twin lead connects to the output of the sensor, and the home-made

Fig.3.13 Leads fitted to the connector

connector can be mounted on the sensor, or at any convenient point on the robot close to the sensor. A standard Lego lead is then used to connect the home-made connector to the RCX unit in the normal way.

Limitation

It is only fair to point out that this type of home-made connector does have a slight limitation compared to the Lego "real thing". This is simply that the

Fig.3.14 The terminals on Lego connectors

home built connectors will only connect properly to the Lego variety in two orientations. No connections are made if the other two orientations are used. To see the reason for this you simply have to look at the Lego connectors. The metal terminals on the male connectors are in the corners, and the metal plates in the female connectors are at the sides, as can be seen from Figure 3.14.

Whichever way round the male connectors are fitted, the terminals in the corners will always make contact with both plates.

The bolt heads of a home-made connector will touch the two plates when fitted one way around, or at 180 degrees to that orientation. With the other two orientations nether bolt head will come into contact with a plate in the other connector. This is not really a major limitation, since the home-made connectors can still be connected to the proper Lego variety with either polarity. You simply have to remember not to connect them in such a way that no connection is made.

Wirier method

The bolt method is a popular one, but in my opinion it is not the best approach to the problem. The main drawback is that it is increasingly difficult to get screws of the right type. The BA sizes are likely to become obsolete in the not too distant future as metrication is finally completed, and cheese head bolts seem to be out of fashion. Round head screws seem to be useless in this application. The panel head variety is a better bet, but these are still far from ideal. There are similar methods using copper tubing and other materials to produce the metal studs, but none of these are particularly easy to implement successfully. It is easier to produce connectors that work a couple of times and then fall apart than it is to produce durable connectors.

My preferred way of doing things is to add pieces of wire into and partially around the spigots of an ordinary Lego brick. This produces something much closer to the Lego "real thing" than most other methods of producing homespun connectors. Figure 3.15 shows a connector of this type, and the wires that provide the connections are just about visible. Making a connector of this kind is admittedly a bit fiddly, but it is probably no more difficult than any other form of home produced Lego connector.

Fig.3.15 A connector made using the wire method

I used 24 s.w.g. (0.56 millimetre diameter) tinned copper wire to make the terminals, but any non-insulated wire of about this size should suffice. This is the only material needed to make one of these connectors, apart from the Lego brick of course. The only other essential items are a drill capable of producing very small holes, and a modelling knife. By small holes I mean about 0.7 or 0.8 millimetres in diameter.

A large power drill is not exactly ideal for this type of thing. One of the smaller cordless drills is better, and a miniature electric drill as used for printed circuit boards, etc., is ideal. Life will be much easier if the drill is fitted in a stand, and there will also be less risk of breaking the drill bit. Drill bits as fine as this are easily snapped, and the various long-life types that are made from very hard materials are particularly vulnerable. As we are only working on soft plastic it is not necessary to use expensive drill bits, and cheap types are more than adequate.

Drilling for coil

Figure 3.16 shows the general scheme of things used with this method, and it shows the brick as if it were transparent so that the two pieces of wire can be seen. Two 0.7 millimetre holes are drilled in each of the spigots that are to

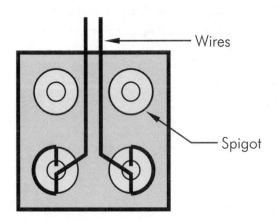

be modified. However, each pair of holes is produced in a single drilling operation. Drilling one of these holes is not difficult, since you have clear access to the spigot on the appropriate side. Drilling the hole opposite this is virtually impossible, since the spigot is obscured on that side by one of the other spigots. Therefore, having drilled the first hole simply go on drilling straight through and out the other side of the spigot. Due to the small size of the drill bit needed for this operation, it might be necessary to have the drill bit something less than fully inserted into the chuck of the drill. This makes the drill bit even more vulnerable to snapping, so go very carefully if you need to do this.

Fig.3.16 Fitting the wires into the brick

If you have a drill in a stand it should not be too difficult to drill the holes. Without the aid of a stand it is a little trickier, but should not be too difficult provided the brick is securely held in a vice. Having drilled the holes you have something like Figure 3.17. Do not worry if it is not absolutely perfect. It is difficult to get things absolutely perfect with something as small and awkward as this. As long as you have two sets of holes in just about the right place the brick will form the good basis of a connector.

For the connector to work it is important that the wires are slightly recessed into the spigots. Unless this is done the female connector will not fit properly onto the home-made type, because the wires will effectively enlarge the spigots too much. Also, the wires will tend to slip out of position with use. Because the bricks are made from quite a soft plastic it is easy to cut the grooves using a modelling knife. The brick

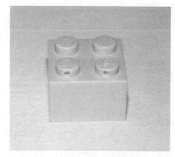

*Fig.3.17 The holes drilled
in the spigots*

should be securely fixed into a vice first, and as always when using a sharp knife, due care must be exercised. Lego MindStorms kits are not recommended for younger children, but any "under-age" MindStorms enthusiasts should enlist the assistance of an adult when making home-made connectors.

When working on such a small scale it is difficult to make a really neat job, but everything should be fine provided there is a small groove around the spigot wherever the wire will fit. Do not cut a deep grove as the wire will then fit right into the plastic and will not make contact with the plates in the female connector. It could also weaken the spigots to the point where the brick would be unusable.

Fitting the wire

You should now have a modified brick of the type shown in Figure 3.18, and it is time to fit the wire. Some adhesive can be used to help keep the wire in place, but I would not recommend doing things this way. One reason for this is that I have not found it necessary, and the wires seem to stay in place very well provided they are pulled firmly tight. Another problem is that any adhesive that finds its way onto the outside edges of the wires will insulate them and prevent the

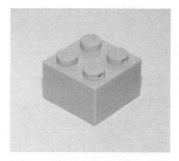

*Fig.3.18 The grooves cut
in the spigots*

connectors from working. The adhesive could probably be scraped away without seriously damaging the wires, but it is easier not to use any adhesive in the first place.

Only very short pieces of wire are needed, but it is difficult to work with wires just a few millimetres long. It is much easier to start with pieces about 50 millimetres or so in length and then trim off any excess wire once everything is in place. Start by fitting one end of the wire into one of the holes in a spigot. The natural tendency is for the wire to go in one side, and then go straight through and out the other side, which is not what we require here. We need the wire to go downwards into the brick, so the end of the wire must be given a definite curve to guide it in the right direction. This end of the wire does not need to go deep into the brick, and it could make things difficult later on if it does.

The other end of the wire is then pushed into the other hole in the spigot, and again the end of the wire should be curved to help the wire go down into the brick. This time we do need the wire to go right down into the brick, because this end of the wire is pulled taut in order to tighten the half loop of wire around the spigot. This tightening can be done by hand, but the wire can be pulled a bit tighter with the aid of a pair of pliers. However, avoid pulling it so tight that the wire snaps, the wire is pulled free, or the brick is damaged. Obviously the loop of wire must be guided into place so that it goes around the correct side of the spigot. While pulling on end of the wire to tighten the loop you must be careful to hold the other end in position. Go slowly and carefully or you will simply pull the wire through the small holes and out of the brick. If it does not go quite right the first time, remove the wire and try again with another piece.

To complete the connector, repeat the process for the other spigot. You should then have something very similar to Figure 3.19, which is ready for testing. First make sure that a female connector will fit properly onto your home-made connector. If everything is just right the other connector should clip on and off quite crisply. If the wire loops stick out excessively, either your connector will not fit properly into the other connector or the two connectors will fit at a

slight angle to one another. If the connectors do
not fit together perfectly, try squeezing the wire
loops and the spigots with a pair of pliers and
pulling the wires a little tighter. If this does not
help it will probably be necessary to remove the
wires, cut the two grooves a little deeper, and
then fit new wires.

*Fig.3.19 The completed
connector*

Once the connectors fit properly mechanically
(Figure 3.20) you can check that a good electrical
connection is being made. This can be done using the same basic method
that was described previously. Connect the unit to an input of the RCX unit
using a standard Lego lead, press the View button until the correct input is

monitored, and then try short
circuiting the two leads on the home-
made connector. The connector is
working properly if this produces an
appropriate change in reading. It is
unlikely that this type of connector
will fail to work electrically, since
problems with the wires protruding
too far are more common than the
wires failing to make contact.
However, if the connector fails to

*Fig.3.20 The connector on the left
needs some further work*

work electrically it probably means that the wire is recessed too deeply into
one or both of the spigots. It is probably best to start "from scratch" using
another brick rather than try to rescue the faulty connector.

Making connections to the two wires of the connector should obviously present
no problems. The two wires are trimmed to length using wire cutters and the
ends are tinned with solder. It is probably as well to fit some pieces of PVC
sleeving over the wires to ensure that they can not accidentally short-circuit.
The solderless approach is also possible. Drill two small holes in one side of
the brick to act as exit holes for the leads, which can then be wired to a

connector block. Again, use pieces of sleeving to insulate the wires where there is any risk of them short-circuiting.

Multi-fit

On the face of it there should be no problem in producing an omni-directional version of this type of connector so that, like the Lego "real thing", it can be connected successfully using any of the four possible orientations. If you

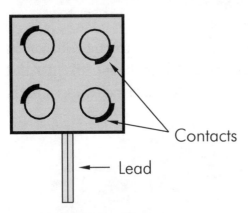

look at one of the Lego connectors it is not too difficult to see how the system works, but Figures 3.21 and 3.22 should make things completely clear. A 2 by 2 brick has a terminal on each spigot, but each terminal only covers about one quarter of each spigot. The positioning of the terminals is crucial, and getting it wrong could produce a short-circuit or simply result in the connector failing to make contact.

Fig.3.21 Positioning of the four terminals on a connector

Figure 3.22 shows how the four terminals are internally connected as two pairs of contacts. In (a) the two plates in the female connector are at the

(a)   (b)

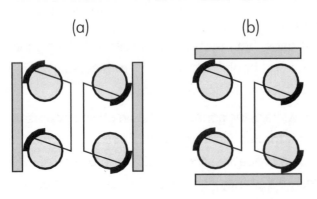

sides, and they connect to two terminals of the male connector. These two connectors are in opposite pairs, so the desired connections are achieved. In (b) the plates have been moved around by 90 degrees. They now connect to two different contacts on the male

Fig.3.22 The female connector always make contact with two terminals

connector, but they still connect to the same pairs of contacts. In other words, the connections obtained in (a) and (b) are effectively the same. If the plates are moved round by a further 90 degrees things are effectively back at (a) again, but the plates connect to the male connector with the opposite polarity. A further shift by 90 degrees takes things back to (b) again, but with a connection of the opposite polarity.

The sensors are normally arranged in such a way that the polarity of the connection is unimportant. Where necessary, the electronics in the sensor automatically adjusts things so that the electronics is fed with a supply of the correct polarity. This is something that is discussed in detail in chapter 4. When making connections to the motors things are more stringent. Two methods of connection have the motor turning in the right direction, and two have it always going the wrong way. It is for this reason that sensors can be connected any old how but care has to be taken when making connections to motors.

Hard wired

Figure 3.23 shows a home-made connector that uses the wiring method described previously, but with two pairs of terminals that mimic a standard Lego connector. This type of home produced connector seems to work well

enough, but making one is a little harder than making the two terminal variety. On the face of it there is no problem in drilling the eight holes required, but this overlooks the fact that two of them are positioned on parts of the spigots that are inaccessible. Access to the appropriate part of the spigot is blocked by one of the other spigots. It is not a good idea to try to get at the target area as best you can, since this is likely to produce a poor finished product. There is a real

Fig.3.23 A four-terminal connector

danger of the drill or you being damaged in the process. The best approach is to simply drill right through the spigot from the opposite side, as when making a two-terminal connector. This leaves an unnecessary hole in the spigot, but the extra hole is of no real consequence.

When drilling the holes be careful to make them at the appropriate places. It is a good idea to use small blobs of paint or ink to act as guides. Having drilled the holes the grooves are cut in the spigots, much as before, but each one covers only one quarter of its spigot. As there are a couple of excess holes, be careful to cut the grooves in the right places. The four pieces of wire are then threaded into place, one by one, pulling each one tight as soon as it is in place.

The four leads must be connected in two pairs (see Figure 3.22), but it is advisable to check that the connector is working before making any permanent connections. Connect your new connector to an input of the RCX unit using an ordinary Lego lead, and check that a change in reading is obtained when the four leads are shorted together and then separated again. This should be repeated with the new connector fitted to the lead with the other three orientations. If all is well the pairs of leads can be trimmed to length and soldered together in the appropriate fashion. If there is a problem it will almost certainly be caused by the wire protruding too far from the spigots. If you look at the connector from above you will easily spot any wire that is sticking out much too far from the spigots. It is then a matter of using pliers to squeeze the wire into place and pulling the wire tight again. If necessary, remove the wire, check that the groove in the spigot is deep enough, and then fit a new piece of wire.

On a plate

So far we have only considered male connectors, but the female variety is also useful. With this type of connector it is possible to connect your sensors direct to the inputs of the RCX unit. It is also possible to directly wire the outputs to devices such as non-Lego motors, actuators, and even something more exotic such as a speech synthesiser. However, it is necessary to proceed with more caution when making female connectors because a botched job could produce something that will damage the connectors on the RCX unit. Never force a home-made connector onto the RCX unit. In fact a Lego "real thing" should never be forced onto the RCX unit either.

In my opinion at any rate, making female connectors is actually a bit easier than producing the male type. If you look at the underside of a female Lego connector you will see that it is not very complex. It consists of what is basically a standard 2 by 2 Lego brick, albeit a somewhat less tall version than normal. The leads are connected to two metal plates at opposite sides of the brick, and it is these plates that connect to the terminals on the male connector. On the face of it, to produce a home-made version it is just a matter of soldering a twin lead to two small plates that are glued inside the brick. In practice it is not quite as simple as this, but it is not very much more involved either.

The first problem is that inside the brick there are two vertical ridges on each side. Both ridges must be removed from opposite sides of the brick to give flat surfaces that the plates can be fixed to easily. The removal of these ridges also makes gaps for the plates to fit into. They would otherwise reduce the empty space inside the brick, probably making it too tight a fit on the RCX unit. The softness of the plastic makes it easy to cut away the ridges using a sharp modelling knife, but take due care when doing this. A hole about 3 millimetres or so in diameter must be drilled in one side of the brick to provide an exit hole for the twin lead. Be careful to drill this hole in a side that will not be used to take one of the plates.

The most difficult aspect of building this type of connector will probably be obtaining suitable sheet metal material for the two plates. Aluminium is not a good choice as it is difficult to make soldered connections to this metal. It can be done using special solders, but even using these it can be difficult to obtain good results. Another problem is that the plate needs to be very thin, and even something like 22 s.w.g. aluminium is likely to be too thick.

Tinplate

The best choice is undoubtedly thin tinplate, but it could be difficult to buy this material. The usual source of supply for do-it-yourself use is an old biscuit tin. Some of the larger boxes of chocolates are actually tins of chocolates and one of these should provide sufficient tinplate for dozens of connectors. Much of the material used in these tins is too thick for our purposes, and it is often shaped as well. However, if you cut out the base you will usually end up with a large flat sheet of very thin tinplate. Even on the larger tins the base always seems to be made from a relatively flimsy gauge of metal.

Tinplate can be cut and worked using normal metal working tools such as hacksaws and files. There are special shears for cutting this material, but the thinner grades can be cut using an old pair of scissors. Do not use a new pair. They will cut the tinplate very well, but they will not remain new for very long! The metal might curl slightly when cut with scissors, but it is easily pressed flat again. Another way of cutting tinplate is to score it deeply using a heavy-duty modelling knife guided by a cutting edge. The metal will soon fatigue and break if it is repeatedly bent backwards and forwards along the score line. Using this method it is easy to produce perfectly straight cuts.

A word of warning is in order here. Some quite sharp edges can be produced when working on tinplate, so always handle it careful, preferably wearing something like carpenters' gloves when dealing with larger pieces. Gloves are not really a practical proposition when dealing with the final plates, which only measure about 12 by 8 millimetres, but most of the sharp edges and corners should have been filed off by then.

The end of the twin lead should be taken through the hole in the brick and then two short pieces of insulation are removed from each of the wires. The bare wires are generously tinned with solder. The middle of each metal plate is also tinned with solder, and this should not be difficult. Provided it is reasonably clean tinplate provides an almost perfect surface for electrical solder. Most wires for electrical use are coated with tin to make them easier to solder. Problems will only occur if the surface is very dirty, and if necessary the tinplate should be cleaned prior to tinning. A wire is then connected to each plate and with the wires and plates both tinned with solder there should be no difficulty in making reliable connections.

To complete the connector the two plates are glued to the sides of the brick. Superglue or any good general-purpose adhesive is suitable. Do not glue the plates in place and then try to make

Fig.3.24 The finished connector

the connections to them. The heat from the soldering iron will rapidly find its way into the brick where it could produce serious damage. Figures 3.24 and 3.25 show a finished connector.

To test the connector it is attached to an input of the RCX unit, which is then used to monitor that input. Short-circuiting the two leads of the connector should produce the usual change in reading. Note that this connector should couple through to the RCX unit when it is fitted with any of the four possible orientations.

I suppose it should be possible to combine the techniques for making male and female connectors to produce a combination of the two, but I have not actually tried this. The Lego connectors are, of course, of this hermaphrodite variety, but for most purposes a connector of one type or the other is all that is needed. It is probably best to keep things straightforward unless there is a genuine need to do otherwise.

Fig.3.25 The home built connector fitted to the RCX unit

Connector plates

Many constructors prefer to make the connectors for their home produced sensors, but this is not strictly necessary. As already pointed out, standard Lego leads can be cut to produce leads and connectors for use with your

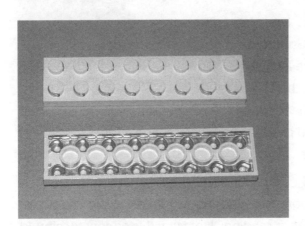

Fig.3.26 The top and under sides of a connector plate

own sensors. Even this is not necessary though, and Lego do actually produce conductor plates that can be used to produce male or female connectors on your add-on devices. Ordinary Lego leads can then be used to connect your gadget to the RCX unit. Other sizes may be produced, but the only conductor plates I have encountered are 8 x 2 plates, and they are supplied

in packs of three plates. Figure 3.26 shows the top side of one plate and the underside of another. On the underside there are two strips of metal that run on opposite sides for the full length of the plate. On the top side there are the usual 90 degree terminals on every spigot. All the terminals in each row are interconnected.

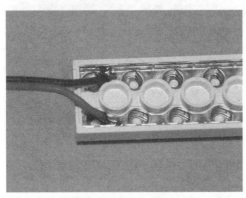

Fig.3.27 Making connections to the metal strips

The normal way of using one of these plates is to mount it on the top of your sensor, with the two leads from the sensor connected to the metal strips on the underside of the conductor plate. It is not difficult to make soldered connections to the strips (Figure 3.27) provided the ends of the wires and the metal strips are tinned with solder first. The joints

must be completed fairly swiftly so
that the plastic does not melt and
cause serious distortion of the plate.
The plate is connected to the RCX
unit via an ordinary Lego connecting
lead that fits onto the top or
underside of the plate. It is also
possible to approach the problem
from the other side, with the leads
being connected to a couple of the

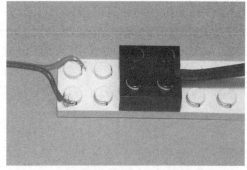

*Fig.3.28 Connections can also be
made to the top of the plate*

terminals on the spigots (Figure 3.28). Again, the connector on the lead can
be fitted on top of or underneath the plate.

The Lego conductor plates probably represent the best way of making
connections from your own devices to the RCX unit. It is certainly worthwhile
buying some of these plus some extra leads if you intend to experiment with
your own sensors and (or) output devices.

4

Ins and outs

Inputs

If you attach do-it-yourself electronics to the RCX unit it will almost invariably be a sensor of some kind. It is possible to drive something other than Lego motors and lamps from the outputs, but the range of options is relatively limited. Using the outputs is discussed at the end of this chapter, but we will mainly be concerned with adding your own sensors to the inputs. A wide range of sensors can be interfaced to the RCX unit, but only a limited number are of general interest and use. The standard Lego sensors are light, touch, angle (rotation), and temperature types, and these cover most requirements. It is possible to make your own versions of these, and there are one or two additional types that can be useful. In particular, an ultrasonic range detector can be particularly useful with ranger type robots. Magnetic sensors and sound detectors also open up some interesting possibilities.

When dealing with do-it-yourself sensors it is essential to understand that they fall into two categories that are interfaced to the RCX unit in rather different ways. The passive sensors are the simplest type, and will usually consist of just a single component. The Lego touch switch is an example of a passive sensor, and it is basically just a mechanical switch that connects directly to the RCX unit's input terminals. Powered sensors, which are also called active sensors, contain some electronics that requires power from the RCX unit.

It is not mandatory to power active sensors from the RCX unit's battery, and a sensor can have its own battery supply. However, in most cases there is no point in having an extra set of batteries, which tends to increase running costs, is less convenient, and adds bulk to the robot. The Lego Light sensor is an

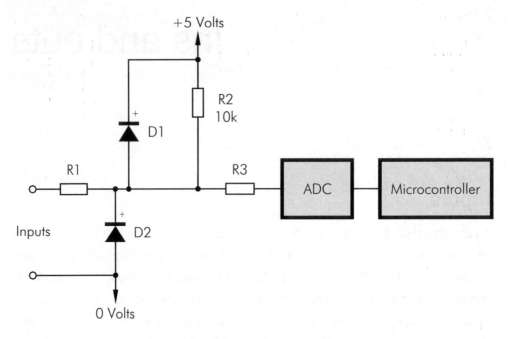

Fig.4.1 The circuit for an RCX input stage

example of a powered sensor. Most active circuits that are used with the RCX unit's inputs are quite simple, using about a dozen components or less. Quite complex circuits can be used though. The main problem with complex circuits is that the sensor could end up larger than the rest of the robot! Do-it-yourself sensors are only practical if they can be kept reasonably compact.

Passive sensors

As the passive sensors are the simpler type we will consider them first. In order to understand how a passive sensor operates it is necessary to consider the input circuit of the RCX unit. The input circuitry is very simple, and is along the lines of Figure 4.1. On the face of it there is no need for any additional components at the input, and the sensor could simply be coupled direct to the input of the analogue to digital converter. This will actually work when using an active sensor that has its own power supply, but it is not appropriate for most types of passive sensor. You have to bear in mind that virtually all passive sensors produce a change in resistance, but the analogue to digital converter in the RCX unit measures voltage.

When used in raw mode an input voltage range of 0 to 5 volts equates to readings from 0 to 1023. The converter is a linear type, so it is easy to work out the reading that should be obtained for a given input voltage. Dividing 1023 by 5 gives the increment per input volt, and this is 204.6. The converter only deals with integers (whole numbers) so the 0.6 is rounded up to give a figure of 205. Simply multiplying the input voltage by 205 gives the reading that should be obtained. For example, 1.6 volts would give a reading of 328 (1.6 x 205 = 328).

With simple sensors producing an output resistance and the converter requiring an input voltage, some means of providing a conversion from one to the other is required. The simplest way of doing this is to connect the sensor and a load resistor across the supply lines so that they form a potential divider. This is the method used here, where R2 acts as the load resistor and the sensor is connected across the two input terminals. Resistors R1 and R3, together with diodes D1 and D2, protect the input from excessive positive or negative voltages. I am not sure if the protection circuit is exactly as shown in Figure 4.1, but it is something along these lines. For the moment we will ignore these components anyway.

With the protection components conveniently forgotten we have the very simple input circuit shown in Figure 4.2. When the sensor is at the same

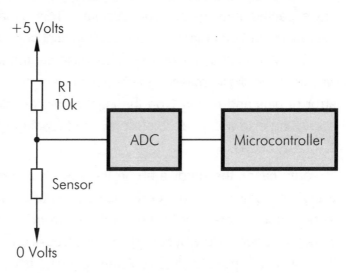

Fig.4.2 Effective input circuit when using a passive sensor

value as load resistor R1 (10 kilohms or 10k), there is half the supply voltage across each element in the potential divider. The output voltage of the sensor circuit is therefore 2.5 volts. If the resistance of the sensor reduces, so does its share of the supply voltage, and the output potential decreases. Conversely, if the resistance of the sensor increases, so does its share of the supply potential. The output voltage of the sensor circuit then increases.

Mathematics

Calculating the output voltage it is just a matter of working out the portion of the total resistance in the potential divider that the sensor accounts for, and then multiplying this by the supply voltage (5 volts). For example, if the sensor has a resistance of 4k, it represents about 0.2857 of the total value (10k + 4k = 14k, 4k/14k = 0.2857). Multiplying this by 5 gives the output potential, which works out at about 1.4286 volts. This figure can be multiplied by 205 to give the reading from the converter, or the reading can be obtained by multiplying 0.2857 by the full-scale reading of the converter (1023). Either way an answer of 292 is obtained.

It is only fair to point out that actual readings will usually be slightly different to any expected readings that you calculate. This is mainly due to component tolerances, but other factors such as electrical noise and slight non-linearity in the analogue to digital converter can also contribute to errors. Due to the way in which digital measuring circuits function there is usually a margin of error of plus and minus 1 on the least significant digit. Therefore, even if everything else was perfect, our predicted reading of 292 could actually be 291, 292, or 293.

In some cases the hardware can include a trimmer control that enables everything to be set up for good results. In other cases some adjustment has to be made to threshold values in the software in order to get everything working properly. However good your sources of data and your mathematics, it is not usually possible to calculate everything accurately enough to obtain perfect results first time. A certain amount of "fine tuning" is usually needed somewhere in order to get everything working to perfection.

Returning to Figure 4.1, one might expect the over-voltage protection components to have a significant bearing on the readings obtained, but in practice their effect is minimal. Input resistor R1 has a low value that has a minimal effect. The resistance in diodes D1 and D2 and the input resistance of the analogue to digital converter could produce losses through R1 and R3, but these stray resistances are too high to have any noticeable effect. R1 is connected in series with the sensor, and effectively raises its value slightly. This factor could have a significant bearing on readings, but in practice it seems to be swamped by other factors such as the tolerances of the components. For most practical purposes any effects of the over-voltage protection circuit can be ignored.

Right choice

Obviously there is a limit to the resistance range that will work with the RCX unit. If you work out the minimum resistance at which the full-scale reading is achieved, and the maximum value that will produce a reading of zero, an impressive resistance range is obtained. Unfortunately, this gives a rather rosy view of things. Using a sensor over a high resistance range gives poor resolution and there can also be problems with pick-up of electrical noise. The noise problem does not occur with a sensor that operates over a low resistance range, but the problem of poor resolution does. Ideally the sensor should have a value of around 10k in normal operation. In other words, its value in normal operation should not stray too far from the resistance of the load resistor at the input of the RCX unit. This should give excellent resolution and problems with noise should be kept at bay.

As an example, suppose that you require a sensor that will enable threshold temperatures of around 25 degrees Celsius to be used. The obvious choice is a thermistor. This is a component that has a resistance that changes dramatically with variations in temperature. All normal thermistors have a negative temperature coefficient, which simply means that their resistance goes down as the applied temperature is increased.

Suppose that you can obtain thermistors having values of 4.7k, 47k, and 470k at 25 degrees Celsius. The 4.7k type has less than half the ideal resistance, but this is near enough to give good results in practice. The 47k component has nearly five times the ideal value, but it would probably still be usable. The 470k thermistor has a resistance nearly 50 times higher than is ideal, and its value is high enough to give serious noise problems. The 4.7k type would therefore be the best choice, the 47k represents a usable second choice, and the 470k type would be unlikely to work well.

Topsy-turvy

It is important to realise that readings from the converter will sometimes operate in an inverted manner. With our temperature-sensing example you might expect increased temperature to produce higher readings. In fact the opposite occurs because the thermistor has reduced resistance when the temperature is increased. The output voltage therefore decreases as the applied temperature increases. This factor does not matter provided you are aware of it and write the software accordingly.

With an active sensor an uncooperative sensing element can be "put to rights" by other circuitry in the sensor. With a passive type you just have to put up with it and effectively provide an inversion in the software. Even with an active sensor you may prefer to sort things out in the software. The Lego light sensor is normally used in percentage mode, which provides an inversion so that higher light levels give increased readings. Things operate the other way round if raw mode is used.

It is also worth making the point that simple passive sensors will not usually produce readings that convert easily into meaningful values. Suppose that our temperature sensor did produce increased readings with increased temperature. A lack of linearity in the device itself and the simple method of resistance to voltage conversion means that there is no easy way of converting returned values into actual temperatures. Simply dividing the value by (say) 20 might give accurate results at 25 degrees Celsius, but at 20, 15, and 10 degrees it might be necessary to divide by 18, 15, and 10.

In practice this is often of no consequence, since it is not really measurement that is required. The robot is required to do something when a certain threshold temperature, light level, or whatever is reached. The usual way of handling this is to have the sensor at the required threshold level and then use the RCX unit to display the returned value. This value can then be used as the threshold level in the control software. If more than one threshold level will be used, this process must be repeated for each level.

Of course, it is possible to apply some mathematics, use lookup tables, etc., to iron out accuracy problems so that accurate measurements can be made. However, it can be difficult and time consuming to obtain good results using these methods. If you require a temperature sensor that can be used for absolute temperature measurement it is probably best to opt for the Lego temperature sensor. The built-in software of the RCX unit enables this to provide reasonably accurate temperature measurement in degrees Celsius or Fahrenheit.

Active sensors

On the face of it there is no way that the RCX unit can provide power to an active sensor since each input port has only two terminals. It would seem that a third terminal is needed in order to provide a power supply output from the RCX unit. It is actually possible to both power a sensor from two terminals and read the device, but it requires a certain amount of trickery. The process operates by alternating the two terminals between acting as supply outputs and sensor inputs. This is potentially a bit risky, and things could go terribly wrong if the supply outputs where even briefly connected to the output of an active sensor. Fortunately there is a simple way of ensuring that this does not happen and that active sensors can operate safely.

The normal way of handling things is shown in the circuit diagram of Figure 4.3. This is actually rather more complicated than it needs to be, but active sensors are normally designed so that, like the passive variety, they can be connected to the RCX input terminals either way round. The sensor circuit

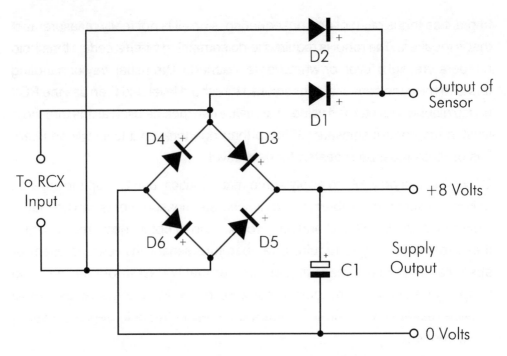

Fig.4.3 The standard supply and input circuit for an active sensor

must be fed with a supply of the correct polarity, and we therefore need a supply circuit that will always steer the supply to the sensor with the appropriate polarity. This is the purpose of diodes D3 to D6. Anyone familiar with basic electronics will recognise these straight away as a bridge rectifier. With the input connected one way round, two of the diodes feed the supply to the output with the right polarity and the other two have no effect. Swapping over the connections to the inputs changes the roles of the two pairs of diodes, and the output is still fed with a supply of the correct polarity.

This still leaves a slight problem, which is that although the supply is present for the majority of the time, it disappears briefly when the input reverts to normal input operation. Fortunately there is an easy way round this, which is to use a smoothing capacitor across the supply outputs (C1). The capacitor charges up while the supply is present, and discharges to maintain the supply during the brief periods when it is removed. The output current of the circuit is not very great and the supply is only discontinued for about 0.1 milliseconds, so a modest value of about 10uF to 100uF is normally adequate for C1.

Note that the output voltage of the supply is typically a little under 8 volts, and is therefore a volt or so less than the 9-volt supply of the RCX unit. This loss is due to the voltage drop of about 0.6 volts or so through each of the two diodes that provide the supply. The voltage provided by the battery in the RCX unit will vary from about 9.5 volts when new to around 7.5 volts when it is nearing exhaustion, so the actual supply voltage could be anything from about 8.3 to 6.3 volts. This change in voltage could seriously reduce the accuracy of the sensor, and where appropriate the sensor circuit must therefore include a voltage regulator.

Incidentally, it is possible to read the battery voltage using the software supplied with the Robotics Invention System. From the Main Menu select Getting Started, and then select Set Up Options from the next screen. This brings up a screen that includes a battery gauge at the bottom. If you position the cursor over the battery gauge a voltage reading will be shown immediately above the cursor.

Another point to bear in mind is that there is a certain amount of resistance in series with the supply output circuit of the RCX unit. When set to operate with an active sensor the input circuit of the RCX unit is something like Figure 4.4. The pull-up resistor (R3 here) is retained, and as we shall see shortly it is essential. The over-voltage protection circuit is also retained, and this ensures that your sensor circuit can not take the input of the converter circuit much above the full-scale value of 5 volts. The supply is obtained via an electronic switch that provides the on and off switching, and this adds a small but significant resistance in series with the supply. This resistance is represented by R1 in Figure 4.4, but in reality it is an innate property of switch S1.

Provided the sensor only consumes a milliamp or two of current the source resistance will not matter too much, but higher currents could result in the supply voltage being reduced by a volt or two. Tests on an RCX unit suggest that the supply will actually reduce by nearly 150 millivolts (0.15 volts) per milliamp of supply current. This equates to a resistance of a little under 150 ohms, but there is probably a significant variation from one RCX unit to another. A sensor that draws 10 milliamps of current will produce a voltage drop of

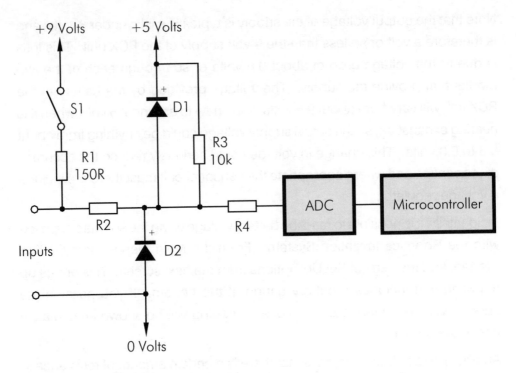

Fig.4.4 The RCX input circuit for when using an active sensor

about 1.5 volts, and this rises to around 3 volts at a current drain of 20 milliamps. Realistically, currents of much more than about 20 milliamps can not be drawn from the RCX unit.

Lost potential

Returning to Figure 4.3, the purpose of diodes D1 and D2 is to enable the output of the sensor to drive both terminals of an RCX input port. Remember that the sensor can be connected to the input port either way around, and there is no way of knowing which is the earth terminal and which is the input terminal. It is not acceptable to simply wire them together, since this would short circuit the two terminals, preventing any signal going in or any power from coming out. A form of diode mixer is therefore used to avoid a short-circuit while enabling the sensor to drive whichever input terminal is the right one. Depending on the polarity of the supply from the RCX unit, one or other of these diodes will block the supply and prevent a heavy current from flowing. In fact no significant supply current will flow through these two diodes.

Although the output of the sensor can drive the appropriate input terminal, the inclusion of a diode in series with the output means that a current can only flow in one direction. In terms of conventional current flow, the diodes prevent the sensor from feeding current into the RCX unit, but it can still flow from the RCX unit into the output circuit of the sensor. The 10k pull-up resistor at the input of the RCX is crucial, because the output of the sensor can not pull the input of the converter higher in voltage, it can only pull it lower. The pull-up resistor therefore does what the sensor can not do, which is to pull the input up towards the +5-volt supply potential. The sensor pulls in the opposite direction, and brings the input voltage down to the apposite figure. The 10k pull-up resistor effectively becomes part of the sensor's output stage.

Unfortunately, there is a major drawback in using a diode in series with the input signal. A theoretically perfect diode would have zero resistance in the forward direction and infinite resistance when reverse biased. Failing that, it would at least have a low and constant resistance in the forward direction and a very high resistance when reverse biased. Modern semiconductor diodes have extremely high reverse resistances, and in this respect they are close to the ideal. In the forward direction the situation is less satisfactory, with a very high resistance being exhibited until the applied voltage reaches about 0.6 volts or so. The resistance then drops rapidly as the applied voltage is increased.

In the present context this means that the sensor circuit can not pull the input voltage of the converter below about 0.6 volts. In effect, about 0.6 volts is added to all input voltages. In practice matters are rather worse than this, because a protection resistor is used in series with the output of the sensor circuit to limit the current that the RCX unit can force into the output of the sensor. This further weakens the ability of the sensor to pull the input of the converter down towards 0 volts. This is not necessarily of any practical consequence, since in most cases the sensor and the RCX unit will not be

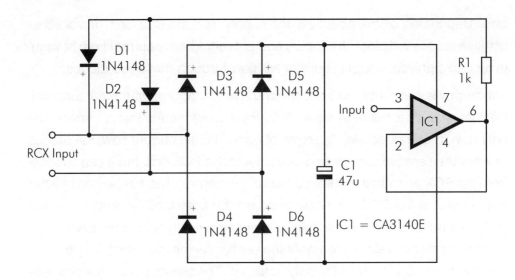

Fig.4.5 *A basic interface circuit for an active sensor*

called upon to make accurate measurements. You simply require something to happen when a certain threshold level is reached, and everything will work fine provided that the correct threshold values are used in the control software. These values can be found by empirical means if necessary.

If the sensor and RCX unit are required to make accurate measurements over a wide range of input voltages it is necessary to do something about the added voltage. The easy way of doing this is to use an offset in the software. It is helpful if we first look at some actual transfer characteristics of driver circuits. Figure 4.5 shows a simple driver circuit added to the basic interface circuit of Figure 4.3. The additional circuit is a simple voltage follower circuit, where the output voltage is equal to the input potential. Although this type of circuit may seem to be something less than useful, the salient point is that the circuit provides massive current gain. The output can drive the input circuit of the RCX unit with no difficulty, but the input requires a totally insignificant drive current. R1 is the protection resistor for the output of operational amplifier IC1.

Note that the operational amplifier used for IC1 must be a type that is suitable for use in single supply d.c. coupled circuits. Many operational amplifiers have a minimum output potential of one or two volts, and if used in this circuit would probably not work at all. The output voltage swing from the circuit would certainly be too small to be of much practical value. The CA3140E specified for IC1 is a type that will work well in this type of circuit and should give output potentials right down to 0 volts, or something very close to it. Incidentally, the CA3140E is a static sensitive device that requires the usual anti-static handling precautions. The two operational amplifiers in an LM358C are suitable for this type of circuit, as are the four amplifiers in an LM324C. Neither of these devices is vulnerable to static charges.

Facts and figures

Figure 4.6 shows a graph that plots the input voltage to the circuit versus readings obtained in raw mode. This clearly shows the problem of the added voltage, with an input potential of 0 volts providing a reading of just over 300. Surprisingly perhaps, linearity is not bad for input voltages of up to about 3.5 volts or so. It should therefore be possible to obtain reasonable accuracy over a wide range of values provided high readings of more than about 950 are not used. The offset of 300 or so can be removed simply by deducting the appropriate figure in the control software. The lowest reading I could obtain was 303, so deducting this from readings would give values that started from zero. Some further mathematics would then be needed to get the scaling right

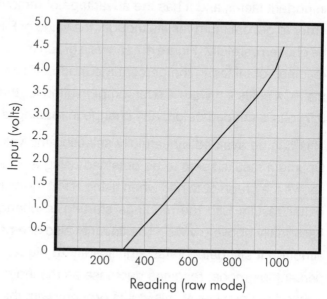

Fig.4.6 *Example input characteristic in raw mode*

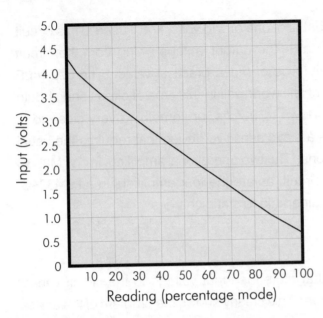

Fig.4.7 *The input characteristic obtained
in percentage mode*

so that readings were in degrees Celsius, millivolts, or whatever.

If you are not trying to make accurate measurements and will only be using threshold values, the percentage mode might be a better choice. The percentage mode is not necessarily a good choice, since readings are being divided by a factor of around 10, which substantially reduces resolution. Percentage mode is certainly a good choice where this is not an important factor, and it has the advantage of removing the offset for you. In order to get optimum results though, the value of R1 in the driver circuit must be chosen carefully. Figure 4.7 shows a graph that plots input voltage against readings obtained in the percentage mode. The clear problem here is that the RCX unit's firmware is overcompensating for the added voltage and over 0.5 volts is needed before any change in reading is obtained.

This can be avoided by carefully selecting the value for output resistor R1. Optimum results seem to be obtained using a value of 2.7k, and Figure 4.8 shows the graph obtained when using R1 at this value. This produces much better results with the readings starting to change with an input voltage fractionally above 0 volts. The linearity also seems to be slightly improved, although it still deteriorates significantly at higher input voltages. With the percentage mode, readings decrease as the input voltage is increased. As pointed out previously, this works properly with the Lego light sensor, which gives reduced output voltage when the light level increases.

Provided the control software is written accordingly, whether readings are inverted or progress in the right direction is irrelevant. On the other hand, most people find it easier to work with readings that go up when the light level, temperature, or whatever, is increased. If the hardware can not easily be designed to give a suitable output signal, simply deducting

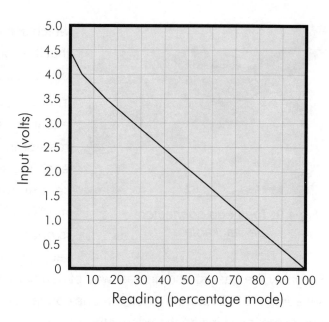

Fig.4.8 Optimum input characteristic for percentage mode

percentage mode readings from 100 will produce right way round readings.

More inputs

Although the three inputs of the RCX unit are adequate for most purposes, there may occasionally be the need for more than three sensors. In the case of a touch sensor it is actually possible to connect more than one to an input of the RCX unit. The Lego connectors are stackable (Figure 4.9), so physically connecting more than one touch sensor to an input is perfectly straightforward. If you try this and use the display to monitor readings from the appropriate input, you will find that operating either of the sensors will produce a change in reading. In theory at any rate, there is no limit to the number of touch sensors that can be used with a single input.

There is a major limitation of this method, which is simply that there is no way of telling which switch has been operated. In some applications this will not be of importance, and the same action will be taken regardless of which sensor has been activated. In most applications though, it is necessary to know

Fig.4.9 The Lego connectors are stackable

which sensor has been operated so that the appropriate course of action can be taken.

There is a way around this problem, and it is merely necessary to add a resistor in series with the switch in each sensor. I would certainly not recommend dismantling and modifying the touch sensors, but this is not really necessary because the resistors can be added externally. Probably the easiest and neatest way of handling things is to connect each sensor to the RCX unit via a home-made connector, with a resistor added into one of the leads inside the connector.

How does the software determine which switch has been operated? The trick is to use a different resistor value for each sensor, as in Figure 4.10. Switches S1 and S2 are actually the sensors, and resistors R1 and R2 are the additional resistors. Switch sensors are normally used with Boolean mode,

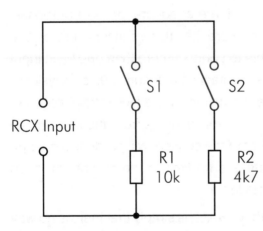

Fig.4.10 A circuit that permits independent operation of two sensors on one input

but raw or percentage mode is needed for multiple sensors connected to a single input. Here we will assume that raw mode is being used. A resistance of 10k is placed across the inputs when S1 is closed, which will take the raw mode reading from 1023 down to about half that value, or around 512 in other words. Closing S2 places a resistance of 4.7k across the input terminals, taking the reading down to about one third of its full-scale value.

This works out at about 341. With a different reading for each sensor it is possible for the software to determine which one has been activated.

It is not a good idea to have the software test for a particular value, since exactly the same reading may not be obtained each time. Instead, the testing routine must look for a small range of values. Suppose that a value of around 512 is normally obtained when a sensor is activated. The software could first check for a value of less than 522, and if that condition is met it could then test for a value of more than 502. If both conditions are met the returned value is between 502 and 522, and the sensor has been activated. The appropriate list of instructions would then be performed. Even if the returned value sometimes drifts slightly from its normal value of 512, this method has sufficient latitude to avoid spurious operations, but it will still detect any real operations of the sensor.

More than two sensors can be used in this way, and the software should be able to reliably detect which sensor has been operated provided the resistor values are chosen to give significantly different readings from each sensor. When two sensors are used it is also possible to detect if both of them have been activated. With both switches closed the two resistors are added in parallel, effectively giving a single resistor of lower value than either of the individual resistors. This gives a lower reading, and the returned value can be found by operating both sensors and using the RCX unit's display to show the value obtained. The software can then test for readings close to this value using the method described previously.

With three or more sensors in use it is possible to use the same basic method to determine if various combinations of sensors have been activated. However, things soon start to get impractical, and it is probably best to use this system with no more than two, or perhaps three sensors.

Other sensors

Using several switch sensors connected to one input is easy enough, but can other types of sensor be accommodated in the same way? The simple answer to this is "no", and you should definitely not try this method with other types

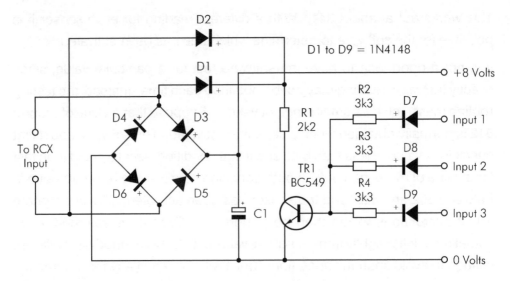

Fig.4.11 A simple gate circuit to accommodate three sensors

of sensor. The protection circuits built into other types of sensor should ensure that no damage occurs, but it is not a good idea to put this type of thing to the "acid test". It would be a pointless exercise anyway, since no meaningful results would be obtained.

With a sensor such as a light type that provides something more than simple on/off levels, there is probably no worthwhile way of reading more than one sensor from a single input. The problem is much more straightforward with a sensor that does provide simple on/off levels, and reading several sensors is then certainly possible. However, it is not just a matter of connecting all the outputs together, and things have to be done in the right way.

Combining several signals to drive one input is really just a matter of using simple logic circuits, but in this context it is probably not worthwhile resorting to logic integrated circuits. Simple discrete circuits based on transistors and diodes are perfectly adequate. Suppose that a robot has three sensors that detect light, temperature, and sound exceeding certain threshold levels, and that the robot must go through a certain routine if any of these levels is exceeded. A single input of the RCX unit and the circuit of Figure 4.11 could be used to monitor all three sensors. The left-hand section of the circuit is the usual supply circuit plus the two diodes to which the input signal is connected.

In this case the input is driven by transistor TR1, which acts as a switch. With all three inputs at a low voltage of about 1.2 volts or less, TR1 receives no significant input current and it is switched off. The pull-up resistor in the RCX unit therefore takes the input to about +5 volts, giving a reading of 0 in the Boolean mode. Taking one or more of the inputs a few volts positive gives a high enough input current to switch on TR1. This pulls the input of the converter to a low voltage, resulting in a reading of 1 in the Boolean mode. Three inputs are shown in Figure 4.11, but any number of inputs can be used. Each input must drive the base of TR1 via a diode and a 3k3 current limiting resistor.

Improved detection

This method has a drawback in that it is not possible to determine which sensor has been activated. This can be achieved using the modified arrangement of Figure 4.12. This circuit works in much the same way as the arrangement of Figure 4.10 that was described previously. Instead of mechanical switches there are three switching transistors (TR1 to TR3) that each drive the input of the RCX unit via a separate resistor. The resistors have significantly different values so that activating each transistor produces a different reading. As in our previous switch sensor example, this enables the software to determine which switch or switches have been activated. The inputs should normally be at a low voltage of under one volt, and they are taken to around 3 to 8 volts to operate their respective switching transistors.

BC549 transistors are specified for the circuits of Figures 4.11 and 4.12, but in an undemanding application such as this virtually any silicon NPN transistor will suffice. Note that PNP transistors are not suitable. Virtually any small silicon diodes will suffice for D1 to D9 as well, and it is not essential to use 1N4148 diodes.

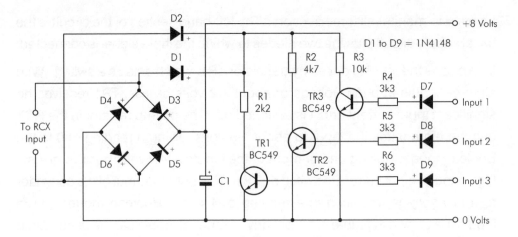

Fig.4.12 A gate circuit that enables independent operation of three sensors

Outputs

The Lego system includes various motors, although it is almost exclusively the geared variety that is used with Lego MindStorms kits. A lamp is also available as an optional extra. It is possible to interface your own devices to the outputs, but the scope would seem to be relatively limited when compared to the possibilities afforded by the inputs. The obvious candidate for use with the outputs is an actuator. This is basically just a coil of wire containing a magnetised metal rod. With power connected to the coil with one polarity the magnetic field produce attraction that pulls the rod into the coil. Reversing the polarity of the power source reverses the polarity of one magnetic field, producing repulsion and sending the metal core out of the coil. In other words, by reversing the polarity of the signal a simple reciprocating action is obtained. This form of movement is better suited to some applications, such as walking robots.

It is certainly possible to drive an actuator from an output of the RCX unit, but you have to bear in mind that the RCX unit has only a limited drive voltage and current available. Model trains and the like normally operate with 12 volt motors that consume about 1 to 2 amps under normal loading. The Lego geared motor seems to operate with very much lower currents and the nominal supply potential is only 9 volts. Under no load a motor only seems to consume a few milliamps, but the current drain increases to around

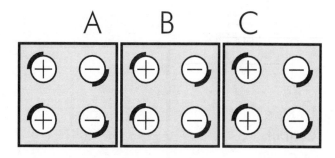

Fig.4.13 *The polarity of the output ports*

100 milliamps (0.1 amps) under heavy loading. Even with the motor stalled the current consumption is only about 200 milliamps.

Although it is possible to drive actuators from the outputs, the actuator must be able to operate from a 9-volt supply and should draw a maximum supply current of about 100 milliamps or so. Unfortunately, this is insufficient to drive most ready-made actuators.

Polarity

Input sensors can be connected to the RCX unit with either polarity, but it is normally necessary to get things the right way round when dealing with the outputs. Get things wrong and motors or actuators will operate in the wrong direction, and electronic gadgets will fail to work at all. Figure 4.13 shows the polarities of the signals on the three outputs of the RCX unit. When connecting electronic circuits to an output of the RCX unit it is a good idea to include some form of reverse polarity protection. In fact this should really be regarded as essential, since it is virtually certain that output devices will occasionally be connected to the RCX unit the wrong way round.

The simplest form of reverse supply protection is a diode included in the positive supply lead, as in Figure 4.14. The diode enables power to flow through to the main circuit if the supply is connected with the right polarity, but it blocks the supply if the polarity is wrong. This protects the circuit from damage, but it will not work unless it is connected correctly. Note that there is

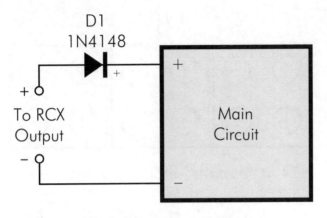

Fig.4.14 A simple method of reverse
polarity protection

a voltage drop of about 0.6 volts or so through the diode and that this slightly reduces the supply voltage to the main circuit.

Another way of handling things is to drive the main circuit via a bridge rectifier, as in Figure 4.15. This is the same method that is used with the RCX unit's inputs when it is used with active sensors. An advantage of this method is that the main circuit will work whichever way round the circuit is connected to the output terminals of the RCX unit. The diodes will always steer the supply to the main circuit with the right polarity.

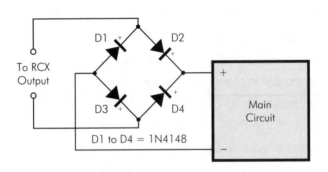

Fig.4.15 With this method the main circuit
will always work, regardless of the
polarity of the connection to the
RCX unit

With a bridge rectifier the supply is obtained by way of two diodes, producing a voltage drop of about 1.2 volts or so. Consequently, the supply voltage for the main circuit is about 1.2 to 1.3 volts below the battery voltage, less any small voltage drop through the output circuit of the RCX unit. This gives a supply potential of about 8 volts with a fresh battery, dropping to only about 6 volts when the battery is near exhaustion.

Power setting

By default the outputs are used at their maximum power setting. If the RCX unit's display is used to show the power level on an output it gives readings from 0 to 8. There are eight power settings from 1 to 8, plus 0, which indicates that the output is switched off. On the face of it the power setting could be used to vary the output voltage, but this will not usually give the desired result. In order to understand the nub of the problem it is necessary to understand the way in which the output power is controlled.

The obvious way of controlling the output power is to simply vary the output voltage. Unfortunately, in practice this method does not work too well when used to control DC electric motors. It varies the speed well enough, but at lower powers the motor has a tendency to stall, and once stopped it is reluctant to start again. The method of power control used by Lego is a form of pulsed control. This operates by sending pulses at full power to the motor so that it is working at full power for a percentage of the time, and is switched off for the rest of the time. If the pulses are sent at too low a frequency the motor will judder along, but provided they are sent at a high enough frequency the motor will run reasonably smoothly.

The motor responds to the average output power, and in the waveform of Figure 4.16(a) the output voltage is switched on for 50 percent of the time, so the motor will receive half power. In the waveform of Figure 4.16(b) the output is only switched on for 25 percent of the time, so the motor is operated at one quarter power. The point of this system is that the pulses at full power resist any natural tendency for the motor to stall. Also, if the motor should stop, or it is being started at a low power level, the pulses will usually nudge a reluctant motor into action. This method of control tends to produce very noticeable "buzzing" sounds from a motor when it is used at low power levels.

Although this system works well with small D.C. electric motors, and possibly with actuators as well, it is not of use with most other devices. In particular, it will clearly not provide a variable output voltage to an electronic circuit. On the face of it the circuit will be switched on and off at high speed by the

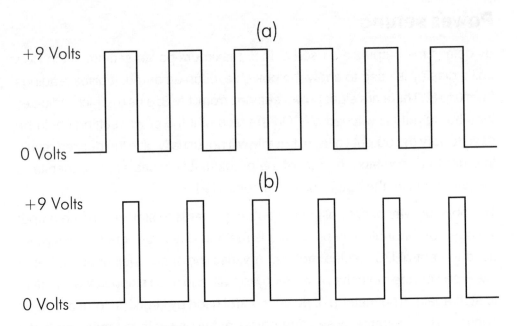

Fig.4.16 Example waveforms for pulsed power control

pulses, but in practice most circuits are fed via a protection diode or a bridge rectifier and will include supply decoupling capacitors. These components, plus the low current drains of most electronic gadgets, result in virtually the peak output voltage being fed to the circuits. There is likely to be a fair amount of supply ripple though, which could prevent some circuits from operating properly.

With the output set at maximum power the output potential is kept at its maximum value continuously. There will still be a certain amount of noise on the output signal, but it is easily filtered out. If a reduction in the supply is needed, say to a standard 5-volt supply potential, this can be accomplished using a 5-volt monolithic regulator. Devices of this type give an accurate and well-stabilised 5-volt supply having a low noise level. Trying to use the power settings to reduce the output potential may fail to do so, and could give a very noisy supply.

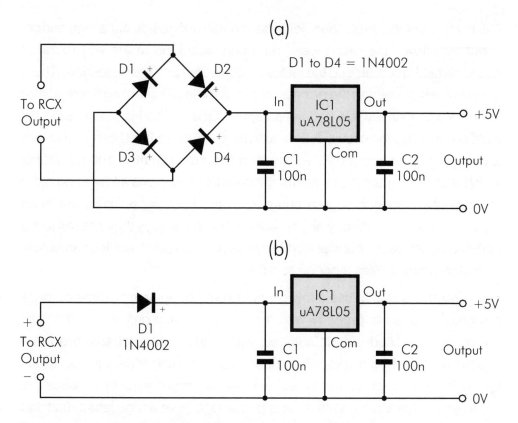

Fig.4.17 *Deriving a stable 5-volt supply from a RCX output port*

Figure 4.17(a) shows a 5-volt regulator driven from an output via a bridge rectifier. This enables the circuit to operate properly regardless of which way round it is connect to the RCX unit. One slight problem with this method is that it will only work if the batteries are reasonably fresh. The input voltage to the regulator is about 1.2 volts less than the battery voltage due to the losses through the rectifier. Most regulator chips have a drop-out potential of about 2 volts, which in this case means that the input voltage must not drop below 7 volts if the output potential is to be maintained. This requires the battery to have a loaded output potential of at least 8.2 volts (7 volts plus the 1.2-volt loss through the bridge rectifier). The circuit of Figure 4.17(b) has a loss of only about 0.6 volts through the protection diode, but requires the circuit to be connected with the right polarity.

The reverse polarity protection could be omitted altogether, but a high current might then flow if the circuit were to be connected the wrong way round. I would certainly recommend the inclusion of reverse polarity protection. There are two ways of keeping the protection circuit while still enabling the regulator to operate properly at low battery voltages. One method is to use Schottky rectifiers in the bridge circuit. A Schottky rectifier such as the 1N5817 produces a voltage drop of about 0.25 volts with a forward current of 100 milliamps, which is the maximum the regulator can handle. This gives a loss of no more than about 0.5 volts through a bridge rectifier. Schottky rectifiers are more expensive than the ordinary silicon variety, but these days they are still just a matter of pence each. It is well worthwhile using this type of rectifier, particularly when the circuit utilizes a bridge rectifier.

The other method is to use a low dropout voltage regulator. Some of these devices can operate properly with the input potential only about 0.2 volts above the stabilised output voltage. Again, these components are more expensive than "bog standard" components, but using them will not "break the bank". It is would seem to be well worthwhile using them in this application. If the two methods are combined it is possible to have a regulator circuit that will operate with a battery voltage as low as 5.7 volts. Since the battery is well and truly flat at around 7 volts, this should ensure that reliable operation of the regulator is provided until the RCX unit shuts down due to inadequate battery voltage.

See the light

Presumably it would be possible to drive an ordinary filament bulb from an output on an RCX unit, but it would have to be a low current type. It would also have to be suitable for operation on 9 volts, which is not a common operating voltage for filament bulbs. A light emitting diode (LED) is probably a better choice, and these can be used with any supply potential of about 3 volts or more. They also have the advantage of low current consumption, with a current of about 20 milliamps normally being sufficient to give good results. This helps to preserve the life of the RCX unit's batteries. The obvious drawback of LEDs is that they produce relatively small amounts of light. With the early LEDs it was difficult to tell whether or not they were switched on when there was even moderately bright ambient lighting!

Fortunately, the best of modern LEDs have greatly improved efficiencies. The cheapest LEDs are not actually much better than the originals, and it is worth paying extra for the higher efficiency types. There is little risk of dazzling yourself when using these LEDs, but the best of them can shine a beam of light that is visible under normal ambient light levels. Another problem with the early LEDs was that you only had a choice of three colours, which were red, red, and red! These days red, green, yellow, orange, and (at a price) even blue LEDs are available. Recently "white" LEDs have also become available, although like the blue variety, they are relatively expensive.

One big advantage of LEDs is that they are physically quite tough, whereas filament bulbs are easily damaged. Another advantage is that LEDs have extremely long operating lives and frequent switching on and off does not significantly affect their life span. Small filament bulbs have operating lives that are measured in hours rather than years, and frequently switching a bulb on and off can significantly shorten its life.

Current limiting

When using LEDs it is essential to understand two big differences in the way LEDs and bulbs are used. A bulb is simply connected to a suitable power source, and it does not matter which way round it is connected. A LED is a true diode and it will only operate properly if it is connected to the supply with the correct polarity. Connect it the wrong way around and no significant current will flow, and it will not light up. A LED will only begin to conduct significantly if the forward bias potential is about 1.7 to 2.2 volts. Raising the applied voltage above this turn-on threshold results in a rapid increase in the current flow.

In practice this means that you can not simply connect a LED directly to the power source. Doing so will produce an excessive current flow that will

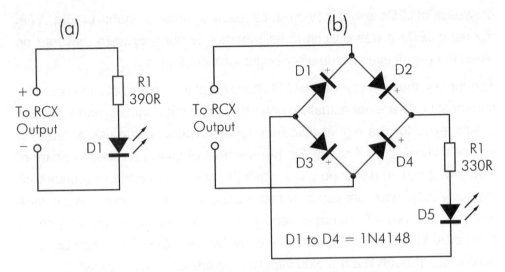

Fig.4.18 *Two methods of driving a LED from an RCX output port*

damage the LED and could also damage the circuit driving it. A LED must be driven from a supply voltage that is significantly higher than the LED's operating voltage, and some form of current limiting circuit must be included to ensure that the LED receives the correct current drive current. A resistor normally provides this current limiting.

The simplest way of driving an LED from an RCX output is shown in Figure 4.18(a). R1 limits the current flow to less than 20 milliamps, which is high enough to give good brightness but low enough to prevent damage to any normal LED. The supply potential is nominally 9 volts, but about 2 volts is needed across the LED (D1) to bias it into conduction. This gives about 7 volts across R1, which gives a current flow of approximately 18 milliamps (7 volts divided by 390 ohms equals 0.0179 amps, or 17.9 milliamps). With a fresh battery the output voltage could be slightly more than 9 volts, but the output current should still be no more than about 20 milliamps. When the battery is nearing exhaustion the voltage across R1 will only be about 5.5 volts, giving a current flow of just 14 milliamps. This is still sufficient to give good brightness from a high efficiency LED.

Note that the circuit of Figure 4.18(a) will only work if it is connected to the RCX unit with the correct polarity. If it is connected the wrong way round it is likely that the maximum reverse voltage rating of D1 will be exceeded. However, this will not result in any damage to D1 provided the current flow is limited to a safe level. R1 will limit the current to no more than a few milliamps, and D1 should be perfectly safe. The circuit of Figure 4.18(b) drives the LED (D5) by way of a bridge rectifier circuit, and it will therefore work when connected with either polarity. The value of current limiting resistor R1 has been reduced slightly to compensate for the voltage loss through the rectifier, and the output current therefore remains much the same at about 18 milliamps.

Colour change

The fact that an LED will only operate with a supply of the right polarity is something that can be exploited. In the circuit of Figure 4.19 there are two LEDs connected in parallel but with the opposite polarity. D1 will switch on if the upper input terminal is positive, and D2 will fail to light up because it is reverse biased. If the upper input terminal is the negative one, the reverse occurs with D2 turned on and D1 turned off. You can therefore switch one LED on and the other off by reversing the "direction" of the output driving the circuit. This is useful, but remember that the two LEDs do not have to be the same colour. By using this technique with LEDs of different colours a switch can be made between (say) red and green lights. If you search through some electronic component catalogues you will

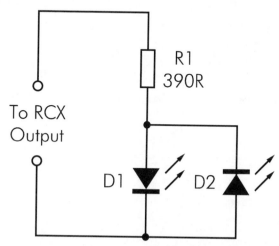

Fig.4.19 *Changing the polarity of the output signal switches from one LED to the other*

probably find one or two bicolour LEDs that use polarity reversal to provide the colour switching. In some circumstances a LED of this type could be more suitable than two separate LEDs.

Light sensors

Double vision

The Robotics Invention System includes a light sensor that, amongst other things, can be used to enable a rover style robot to follow a line on the floor. It is possible to achieve line following using a single sensor, but it is difficult to devise a system that combines rapid movement along the line with reliable tracking. You tend to end up with either a system that tracks with good reliability but gives slow progress, or one where the robot moves along at a reasonable rate but soon "makes a run for it". Matters are very much easier if the robot has two sensors that are positioned on opposite sides of the guideline.

Suppose that the robot is tracking a white line on a dark background. With the robot positioned with the sensors on opposite sides of the line it is easy to get it to track the line efficiently. Normally both sensors are over the dark background and will provide low light readings. If the left-hand sensor suddenly produces a high reading it is over the line, and the robot must turn to the left. Conversely, if the right-hand sensor returns a high reading it means that this sensor is over the line, and the robot must turn to the right to stay on course.

This gives more efficient tracking than a single sensor, which has to be positioned over the line. The robot's control software then tries to keep the sensor over the line. The problem in using a single sensor is that the control software does not know in which direction the robot has strayed when the sensor moves off the line. Tracking the line involves a certain amount of trial and error, with time being wasted when the robot is sent in the wrong direction. Having gone the wrong way, even more time is lost when the robot has to retrace its steps.

Simple DIY sensor

Additional Lego light sensors can be purchased, or you can make your own light sensors. The do-it-yourself approach is likely to be somewhat cheaper and you can have some fun making the sensors. On the other hand, do-it-yourself versions will probably not be quite as neat and professional as the ready-made "real thing", but they should still work very well. The most basic of light sensors can consist of nothing more than a cadmium sulphide photo-resistor mounted on a Lego brick and wired to an input of the RCX unit. A sensor of this type is purely passive and does not require a power supply provided by the RCX unit. Most cadmium sulphide cells will work with the RCX unit, but some work better than others. One having a resistance of a few kilohms at normal ambient light levels is likely to give the best results.

The ORP12 was for many years the standard choice for an application such as this, but the ORP12 is less widely available than it once was, and its relatively large size makes it something less than ideal in the current context. Figure 5.1 shows an ORP12 and a more modern photo-resistor, an MPY76. The ORP12 is more expensive than most of the modern alternatives, so it makes sense to use a modern miniature cell wherever possible. Component catalogues do not always list the photo-resistors by type number, but instead quote a maximum resistance at a light level of 10 lux. A

Fig.5.1 An ORP12 (right) and a MPY76 photocell

component having a maximum resistance of anywhere from about 10 to 100k at 10 lux should be suitable. Even outside that range it is quite possible that perfectly usable results will be obtained.

Sensor with LED

One obvious drawback of a basic sensor based on a cadmium sulphide cell is that it will not work properly in a line-following application under dark conditions. The Lego light sensor overcomes this problem by including an LED that provides a certain amount of light immediately in front of the sensor. Provided the sensor is quite close to the floor this ensures that the light reflected back to the sensor is sufficient to give a change in reading when the sensor moves on or off the line. It is quite straightforward to

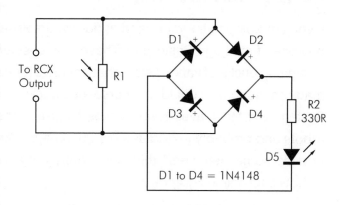

Fig.5.2 A simple light sensor circuit

add an LED to a basic sensor based on a cadmium sulphide cell, and a circuit for a sensor of this type is shown in Figure 5.2.

D1 to D4 form a bridge rectifier that provides LED D5 with a supply of the correct polarity. The sensor can therefore be connected to the RCX unit with any of the four possible orientations. Resistor R2 limits the drive current for the LED to no more than about 20 milliamps. An LED having a diameter of 5 millimetres or more would probably give significantly more light output than a 3-millimetre type. However, if the sensor is to be fitted into a 4 by 2 brick, like the Lego light sensor, a 3-millimetre LED is a more practical choice. It is unlikely that a 5-millimetre LED could be accommodated without using a larger casing. I would suggest using the highest efficiency 3-millimetre LED you can find, even if it does cost more than a "bog-standard" component.

R1 is the photo-resistor, and it is connected straight across the input terminals of the RCX unit. This means that it receives power from the RCX unit for the majority of the time. As this component is basically just a simple resistance this is of no practical importance, and it will not prevent the sensor or the RCX unit from functioning normally. The cadmium sulphide cell is certainly in no danger of being damaged by the supply from the RCX unit.

Sensor construction

If you are going to try your hand at do-it-yourself sensors it is a good idea to buy one of the Lego Basic kits. These only cost a few pounds, and provide numerous bricks of various sizes that are ideal for use as the cases for home-made sensors. You could, of course, use bricks from the Robotics Invention System, but this leaves fewer pieces for use in the basic structure of your robots and probably invalidates the guarantee. Buying a Lego Basic kit will provide some "leftovers" that will slightly enhance the capabilities of the Robotics Invention System.

The cadmium sulphide light sensor can just about be fitted into a 4 by 2 brick, like the "real thing", but I am not going to pretend that it is easy to do this. I

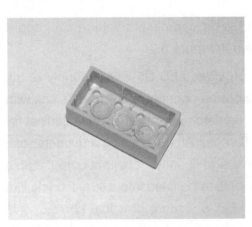

Fig.5.3 The hollowed out brick

suppose that it is not that difficult either, but it is decidedly fiddly, and it certainly helps if you have nimble fingers. The 4 by 2 brick must be hollowed out to make space for the miniature circuit board. First the three round pieces of plastic are drilled out using a drill bit of around 7 to 8 millimetres in diameter. Fix the brick firmly in a vice before you start drilling, and go at things slowly and carefully.

Lego bricks are made from a fairly soft plastic, and you will destroy the brick if you go at things "hammer and tongs" with a powerful electric drill. A hand drill or one of the smaller cordless drills is more suitable for this type of thing. Figure 5.3 shows a 4 by 2 brick with three pieces of plastic removed. There may be some ridges of plastic on the sides of the brick, and these could prevent the circuit board from fitting into place. If necessary, any ridges should be carefully cut away or filed flat.

The cadmium sulphide cell is mounted at one end of the brick, and this becomes the front of the sensor. The cadmium sulphide cell requires two small mounting holes of about 1 millimetre or so in diameter to take the two leadout wires. The cell is glued in place using superglue or any powerful adhesive that is suitable for use with plastics. The LED requires a 3-millimetre diameter mounting hole. A slot for the flying lead is filed at the other end of the brick using a miniature file, or "needle" file as this type of tool is sometimes called. I would advise completing the circuit board before doing this drilling and filing, since you can see exactly where everything must go once the board has been completed.

Circuit board

Details of the component layout for the circuit board and the other wiring are shown in Figure 5.4. The underside view of the board that shows the breaks in the copper strips appears in Figure 5.5. Actually, in this case there is just one break in the strips. The board has 10 holes by five copper strips, and a piece of this size must be cut from a larger board using a hacksaw or junior hacksaw. Do not try to cut between rows of holes because they are too close together. Instead, cut along rows of holes using a minimum of pressure.

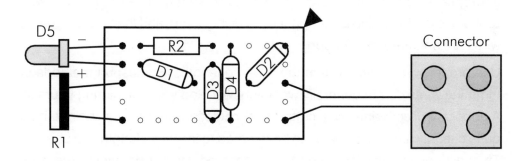

Fig.5.4 The component layout and wiring for the light sensor

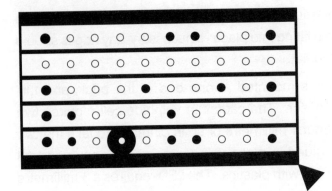

Fig.5.5 The underside of the stripboard

Some makes of stripboard are quite brittle and the board might crack or even shatter if you are not reasonably careful. The sawn edges of the board might be quite rough, but they are easily filed to a neat finish. It might be necessary to do some further filing in order to get the board to fit into the brick, but it should do so provided the brick has been hollowed out properly.

There is a special tool for cutting the strips, which is often called a "spot face cutter" in the electronic component catalogues. This is the easiest way of making reliable breaks in the strips, but a handheld twist drill bit of about 5 millimetres or so in diameter does the job quite well. Make sure that the strip is cut across its full width, but do not get carried away and practically drill a hole through the board!

The board is then ready for the components to be fitted. The traditional approach to using stripboard, and the one utilized here, is to fit the components on the side that does not have the copper strips. This is usually referred to as the top side of the board. The component leads are fitted through the appropriate holes in the board, trimmed to leave a millimetre or two of wire protruding on the underside (copper side) of the board, and then the protruding wires are soldered to the copper strips.

Use proper wire cutters to trim the wires to length. Homespun methods of trimming wires do not generally work very well and you risk injuring yourself. A good pair of combined wire cutters and insulation strippers can be obtained quite cheaply and enable wires to be trimmed to the exact length you choose. They also enable the insulation to be removed without damaging the wire, which avoids the likelihood of the wire snapping later on in the proceedings.

Note that the diodes must be connected with the correct polarity, but the resistors can be fitted either way around. The ordinary diodes have a band at one end of the body, and this indicates the end of the component that carries the cathode (+) leadout wire. This band is included on each of the ordinary diodes in Figure 5.4, so you just have to make sure that the actual components match up with their counterparts in Figure 5.4. The cathode (+) lead of an LED is normally indicate by that leadout wire being slightly shorter than the anode lead. Also, the body is normally flattened slightly next to the cathode lead.

Initially, single-sided solder pins are fitted to the board at the points where the connections to R1, D5, and the connector will eventually be made. These pins will probably extend something like 5 millimetres above the board, which is a bit too much in the current context. The tops of the pins should be cut away using wire cutters, so as to reduce the height of the pins by about half. Tin the tops of the pins with plenty of solder, and it should then be easy to connect wires to them later on.

Practice makes perfect

If you are new to electronics construction this additional advice should be of assistance. There is a slight problem when soldering components to circuit boards, and this is the need for three hands! You need one hand to hold the circuit board, another to hold the soldering iron, and a third to feed in the solder. Most electronic hobbyists soon find a way around this problem. There are actually printed circuit construction frames that use a clamp and some foam material to hold everything in place with the board mounted up-side down. Both hands are then free to hold the soldering iron and the solder. With a tiny board such as this, using a printed circuit frame would definitely be a case of using a "sledgehammer to crack a nut". Probably the best way of tackling the problem is to use some Bostik Blu-Tack, Plasticine, etc., to hold the components in place. With the board turned so that the copper side is uppermost, the Blu-Tack or Plasticine can be used to fix the assembly to the worktop while the soldering is carried out.

If you are new to electronic construction it is advisable to practice soldering before starting in earnest on the light sensor, or any other electronic project. Try soldering some pieces of 24 s.w.g. (about 0.56 millimetre diameter) tinned copper wire to a scrap of stripboard. It is probably worthwhile sacrificing some low-cost components such as resistors by soldering them to the scrap of stripboard as well. Once you are able to produce reasonably neat and reliable soldered joints you can progress to making up a real circuit board.

Small is beautiful

For soldering small electronic components a small electric iron having a rating of about 15 to 20 watts is needed. Most small soldering irons are supplied with a miniature bit of around 3 millimetres in diameter. For the intricate work involved when building sensors for the Robotics Invention System an even smaller bit of around 1.6 to 2.3 millimetres in diameter is probably better, but not essential. Only use solder that is specifically intended for electrical and electronic work. This type of solder is usually made from an alloy that is comprised of 60 percent tin and 40 percent lead, with multiple cores of flux. The flux helps the solder to flow properly over the joint, and it also helps the solder make good contact with the wires if they are contaminated with a certain amount of grease and dirt.

Soldering is not particularly difficult, but like any skill you can not expect to master it in a matter of seconds. With practice you should soon be reasonably proficient and ready to start building. The most common mistake, and one that must definitely be avoided, is to melt some solder on the tip of the iron and then try to transfer it to the joint. This may seem to be a reasonable way of doing things, but it more or less guarantees poor results. One problem with this method is that the flux in the solder burns away on the tip of the iron and there is very little left by the time the solder reaches the joint. With an absence of flux the solder does not flow over the joint as well as it should, and any dirt on the metal surfaces to be joined could easily result in a poor electrical connection.

Another problem is that the metal surfaces are cold, and rather than flowing over them, the solder tends to rapidly solidify on contact. Always apply the iron to the joint first so that the two pieces of metal are heated. The bit of the iron only needs to be applied for about half a second to a second before the solder is fed in and the joint is completed. A good

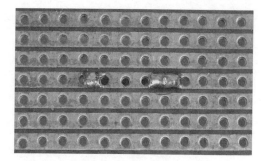

Fig.5.6 Good (right) and bad soldered joints

soldered joint should have a neat mountain-like shape, as in the right-hand joint of Figure 5.6. A "dry" joint is more irregular with an obvious lack of solder, as in the left-hand joint of Figure 5.6. With bad joints the solder sometimes has a dull or even crazed appearance, whereas good-quality joints normally have a shiny finish.

Use enough solder to thoroughly cover the metal surfaces, but do not get carried away. Particularly when using stripboard, excess solder can cause major problems. If you are not careful the solder will spread over two or even three copper strips. Even if you are careful there will be inevitably be the occasional problem with short-circuits between strips due to small trails or blobs of excess solder. It is a good idea to clean any excess flux from the underside of the board and then thoroughly examine it with the aid of a magnifying glass or loupe. There are special cleaning fluids for removing flux, but scrubbing the board with something like an old toothbrush does the job very well. If a short-circuit is discovered it will probably not be too difficult to clear it using the hot bit of the soldering iron. While checking the board, make sure that any cuts in the copper strips have been made properly.

Finishing off

The completed circuit board should look something like Figures 5.7 and 5.8, which respectively show the component and copper sides of the board. At this stage the connector lead and D5 are connected to their respective pairs

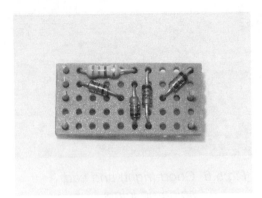

Fig.5.7 The component side of the completed circuit board

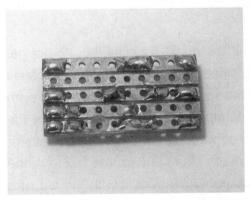

Fig.5.8 The underside of the circuit board, showing the single break in the strips

of solder pins. The leads of D5 must be cut very short since there will be very little gap between the front edge of the board and the front of the casing. Try to solder this component to the pins swiftly and efficiently so that strong joints are produced, but the LED is not in danger of being roasted. With the drilling and cutting of the casing completed, and R1 mounted on the front of the case, the circuit board is slid into place, with D5 fitting into its hole in the front of the case. The leads of R1 are then trimmed to length and connected to the appropriate pair of pins on the board. R1 can be connected either way round. This completes the light sensor, which should then look something like the interior view of Figure 5.9 and the exterior view of figure 5.10. A 4 by 2 plate can be added to the underside of the case to give a neater appearance and keep the dust out.

The finished sensor can be tested by connecting it to an input of the RCX unit, and then pressing the View button until the display monitors the correct input. The input must be set for use with a light sensor if the LED is to be used. It will not light up if the input is set for use with a passive sensor, since the input will not act as a power source. Placing the cadmium sulphide cell in various light levels should produce a wide range of readings. In fact it will probably produce a wider range of readings than the Lego light sensor. In order to obtain operation over the widest possible range of light values with optimum resolution, raw mode should be used instead of percentage mode.

Fig.5.9 *Inside view of the finished light sensor*

When using this type of sensor it is important to bear in mind that the cadmium sulphide cell is omni-directional, whereas the phototransistor in the Lego light sensor has a built-in lens that gives it a relatively narrow angle of view. This is not just of academic importance, and it is a factor that certainly has to be borne in mind when using a sensor of this type for line following. In order to obtain good results it is essential to have the cell quite close to the ground. In fact it should be within a few millimetres of the ground. The

Fig.5.10 *The finished light sensor*

reading from the sensor should then change substantially when it is moved over the line and back again. If the sensor is too far from the ground the readings will become swamped by the ambient lighting, giving little change in the reading when the sensor is moved over or away from the line. The sensor can be made more directional by adding a tube at the front to mask the photocell from ambient light, and you might like to experiment with this.

Components list

Resistors

R1   MPY76 cadmium sulphide cell, or similar (see text)

R2   330R, 0.25 watt 5% carbon film (orange, orange, brown, gold)

Semiconductors

D1 to D4   1N4148 (4 off)

D5   3-millimetre high brightness LED

Miscellaneous

4 by 2 Lego brick for case

0.1-inch pitch stripboard having 10 holes by 5 strips

Lego lead and connector

Single-sided solder pins

60/40 tin/lead multicore solder

The values of small resistors are normally marked using a simple system of colour coding rather than using alpha-numeric characters. For the benefit of those who are unfamiliar with resistor colour codes the component lists in this book include the four-colour code for each resistor.

Directional sensor

Where a highly directional sensor is required it is best to use a different form of light sensor. Photodiodes and phototransistors having built-in lenses are available, and these mostly provide a reasonably narrow angle of view. Both types of component are suitable for our purposes, but the higher sensitivity of phototransistors has the advantage of keeping things as simple as possible. This is especially important if you wish to build a light sensor into a 4 by 2 or 6 by 2 Lego brick, which gives little space for components.

Phototransistors are available in a variety of shapes and sizes, but due to the space limitations only the smallest types are suitable for our purposes.

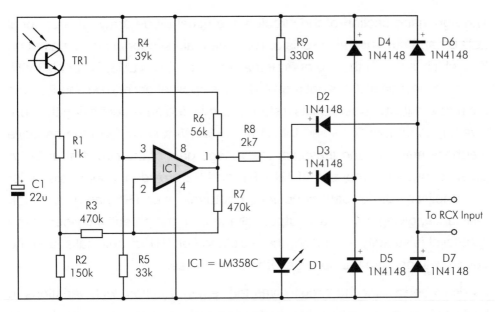

Fig.5.11 The circuit diagram for a versatile light sensor

Probably the most suitable type are the components that look very much like 3-millimetre LEDs, but in a clear encapsulation. I used an SFH309/5, but any similar component should work equally well. Components of this type have only two leadout wires, which are the emitter and collector. The base terminal is not accessible, but in most circuits it is left unconnected anyway. Its absence is certainly of no consequence with the designs featured in this publication.

A cadmium sulphide cell can be used as a simple passive sensor that requires no additional components unless light output from an LED is also required. Wide ranges of light values are covered when using most photo-resistors with the RCX unit. Matters are less straightforward when using a phototransistor. The sensitivity of most phototransistors is too low to permit them to operate as passive sensors with the RCX unit, and unlike cadmium sulphide cells, they only work properly if they are fed from a supply of the correct polarity. It seems to be difficult to obtain good results over a wide range of light levels. Figure 5.11 shows the circuit diagram for a light sensor based on a phototransistor, and this design does manage to cover a useful range of light values.

The right-hand section of the circuit is the usual diode array, plus optional LED D1 and current limiter resistor R9. The main sensor circuit is based on IC1, which is one of the two operational amplifiers in an LM358C or LM358N. The other section of IC1 is not required in this application, and no connections are made to it. IC1 operates as a standard inverting amplifier having the non-inverting input (pin 3) biased by R4 and R5. R3 and R7 form the negative feedback network, and these set the voltage gain of the circuit at unity. A potential divider comprised of TR1, R1, and R2 provide the input signal for the amplifier. Under dark conditions phototransistor TR1 has a very high resistance, giving only a low output voltage from the potential divider. If the light level is steadily increased, the resistance of TR1 steadily falls, and the output voltage from the potential divider increases.

As described so far the circuit gives the required action, with variations in light level being converted into changes in output voltage. However, changes in output potential are only produced over a relatively limited range of light levels. R6 introduces feedback from the output of IC1 to TR1 that enables a wider range of light values to be covered. As the light level is increased, the resistance of TR1 reduces, the output from the potential divider increases, and the output voltage from IC1 reduces. Bear in mind here, that IC1 is used in the inverting mode, a factor that is crucial to the operation of this circuit. As the output voltage of IC1 reduces, R6 increases the loading on TR1 and reduces the sensitivity of the circuit. In other words, as the light level increases, the sensitivity of the circuit decreases. A wide range of light values is thus compressed into a relatively small range of output voltages.

This arrangement gives good control over the range of light levels covered. The value of R2 largely determines the general range covered. A higher value moves the coverage into a lower range of light levels, and a lower value provides coverage of a higher range. The value of R6 determines how much the coverage is broadened. A high value has little effect, and a lower value further broadens the range. A low value for R6 also tends to pull the coverage into a higher range of light levels, so a certain amount of juggling with these values is needed in order to get things just right.

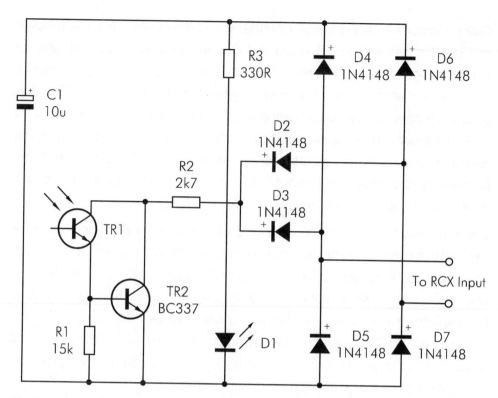

Fig.5.12 A simple but effective light sensor circuit

Simplified version

It is probably impossible to build the circuit of Figure 5.11 into a small Lego brick unless you have access to the components and facilities needed to produce surface mount printed circuit boards. It could be tackled using conventional construction techniques and a larger case, perhaps with the LED and phototransistor mounted in a Lego brick and connected to the main unit by way of a cable about 150 millimetres long. The simplified version of Figure 5.12 is a better bet if you require a sensor that can be made quite small. This circuit can just about be squeezed into a 6 by 2 Lego brick.

The right-hand section of the circuit is, as before, the usual diode array and the LED plus its current limiter resistor. The sensor circuit consists of phototransistor TR1 driving a simple common emitter amplifier (TR2). Under dark conditions TR1 has a high resistance, and little base current is supplied to TR2. Consequently, TR2 passes only a small collector current, and the output voltage of the circuit is relatively high. In higher light levels TR1 conducts more heavily, which in turn produces a higher current flow through TR2. This pulls the output voltage lower, giving an increased reading if the input of the RCX unit is used in percentage mode. As the voltage at the collector of TR2 is pulled lower, the voltage across TR1 is reduced. To some extent this counteracts the increased current flow through TR1 and helps the circuit to cover a wider range of light values.

The sensitivity of the circuit is governed by the value of R1. Increasing the value of this component produces a downward shift in the range of light levels covered. Reducing the value of R1 has the opposite effect. Unfortunately, this circuit has no equivalent to R6 of Figure 5.11, and there is no way of broadening or narrowing the range covered. Note that although TR2 is specified as a BC337, practically any silicon NPN transistor is suitable. It does not need to be a high gain device, and a low gain transistor will probably give coverage of a broader spread of light values.

Construction

Construction of this sensor follows the same general lines as construction of the photo-resistor light sensor. The component layout and wiring are shown in Figure 5.13, with the underside of the board shown separately in Figure 5.14. The stripboard measures 15 holes by five strips, and there are four breaks in the copper strips. Fitting the board into a Lego brick creates problems because the maximum height that can be accommodated is strictly limited. The component layout of Figure 5.13 shows where everything goes on the board, but in order to fit the completed circuit board into the hollowed out brick it will be necessary to mount some of the components in unconventional ways in order to minimise the height of the board.

TR2 must be mounted with the flat side of the case as close to the board as possible, with the leadout wires bent at right angles so that they fit into the

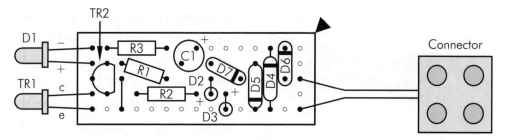

Fig.5.13 The component layout and wiring for the light sensor

holes in the board. Diodes D2 and D3 are mounted vertically. Remember that the cathode (+) lead of a diode is indicated by a band marked around that end of the body. The polarity of D2 and D3 is indicated by "+"

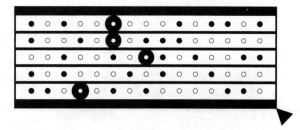

Fig.5.14 The underside of the circuit board

symbols in Figure 5.13. Once fitted on the board these two diodes must be carefully pushed over sideways so that they lie almost flat against the board. Be careful to ensure that no leadout wires are allowed to come into contact with each other.

The cathode lead of D1 is indicated by that lead being slightly shorter than the other one. The same method is used to indicate the collector (c) terminal of phototransistor TR1. If it is to have any worthwhile effect D1 must be a high brightness type, and preferably one of the ultra-bright LEDs that are now available. D1 and TR1 can be mounted on the circuit board via solder pins, but this light sensor has a little more room available in the case than the cadmium sulphide type described previously. If

Fig.5.15 The completed circuit board

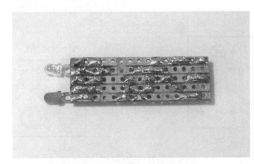

Fig.5.16 The underside of the stripboard panel

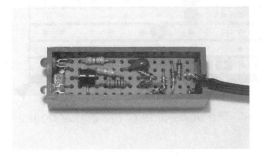

Fig.5.17 The completed light sensor

preferred, D1 and TR1 can be fitted direct onto the board with their leadout wires bent at right angles. The leads must still be very short, as there is only a very few spare millimetres available to accommodate them.

The completed circuit board should look something like the top and underside views of Figures 5.15 and 5.16. One end of the 6 by 2 brick is drilled with two holes for D1 and TR1, and a slot for the lead to the connector is filed at the other end of the case. The circuit board is then slid into the case (Figure 5.17), and a 6 by 2 plate can then be fitted on the brick to seal the case. This gives the completed sensor of Figure 5.18. The RCX unit's display and the View facility can be used to check that the sensor is working properly.

Fig.5.18 Exterior view of the completed sensor. An 8 by 2 plate is added on the underside to provide the sixth side of the case

Components list

Resistors, all 0.25 watt 5% carbon film

R1   15k (brown, green, orange, gold)

R2   2k7 (red, violet, red, gold)

R3   330R (orange, orange, brown, gold)

Capacitor

C1 10μ 16V miniature PC electrolytic or tantalum bead

Semiconductors

TR1   SFH309/5 or similar

TR2   BC337 or similar

D1   High brightness 3-millimetre LED

D2 to D7   1N4148 (6 off)

Miscellaneous

0.1-inch stripboard having 15 holes by 5 copper strips

6 by 2 Lego brick for case

Lego connector and lead

Single-sided solder pins

Solder

Rover robot

Obviously any rover style robot can be used to try the light sensors in applications such as white and black line tracking. The robot featured here is used to demonstrate line following, but is also used throughout this book when a rover style robot is required. It has the advantage that the software examples should work in conjunction with this design with little or no "fine tuning". If you decide to "do your own thing" it might be necessary to make significant changes to the example software in order to get everything working

Fig.5.19 Front view of the rover style robot

perfectly. This design is not particularly compact, but it has space for sensors, etc., at the front, the rear, and amidships on the underside of the vehicle. It can therefore handle most eventualities.

Although it is not the smallest robot of its type, it is still quite manoeuvrable. Steering is accomplished by having separate motors to drive the two main wheels. Strictly speaking it is a four-wheeled vehicle, but the two wheels at the front are mounted close together on a common shaft, and they really form one wide wheel. This effectively makes the robot a three-wheeled vehicle.

Figure 5.19 and 5.20 show two views of the completed vehicle, and the front wheel assembly can be seen in these. In operation it appears as though the vehicle is being steered by the front wheels, but the front wheel assembly is

Fig.5.20 The robot has a rear platform that can accommodate sensors

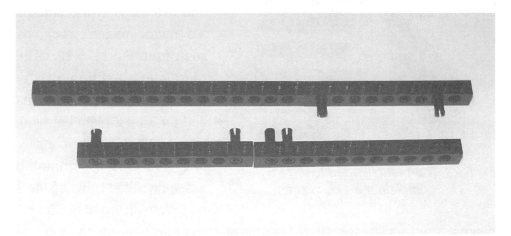

Fig.5.21 One of the side sections ready for assembly

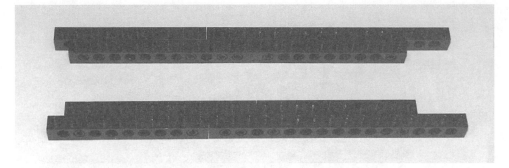

Fig.5.22 The completed upper pieces of the side sections

actually pivoted so that it can adjust to suit the direction in which the vehicle is moving. The front wheels respond to changes in the direction of the vehicle rather than the other way round. This system gives good manoeuvrability and a tight turning circle.

Step 1 (Figures 5.21 to 5.24)

Construction starts with the chassis, and the two side sections of the chassis are built first. For each of these you require six black pegs, a 16 by 1 beam,

Fig.5.23 The parts needed to complete the side pieces

two 10 by 1 beams, and a 12 by 1 beam. Figure 5.21 shows how these are joined together. The two sides of the chassis are "mirror images", as can be seen from Figure 5.22. The rear lower section of the chassis consists of six beams and an 8 by 2 plate per side. Figure 5.23 shows the parts for one side plus a completed assembly. Start by fitting the 8 by 2 plate on top of two 8 by 1 beams. Then add the two 10 by 1 beams on top of the plate, and the two 6 by 1 beams underneath the 8 by 1 beams. These subassemblies are then fitted

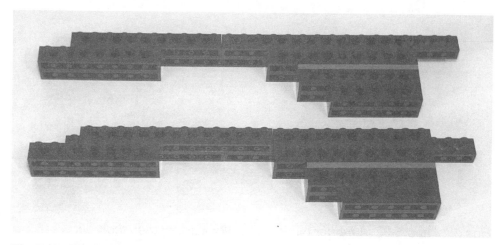

Fig.5.24 The finished side sections

to the side pieces, and two 8 by 1 beams are fitted at the front of each side section. The completed side sections are shown in Figure 5.24.

Step 2 (Figures 5.25 to 5.29)

The two halves of the chassis are now joined together. They are joined at the rear using a 6 by 1 beam between the two sections and an 8 by 2 plate on top (Figure 5.25). At the front there is a similar arrangement using another 6 by 1 beam plus an 8 x 1 plate and an 8 x 2 type (Figure 5.26). Note that the 8 x 2 plate must be one that has holes, since the middle hole takes the front wheel assembly. Another 8 by 2 plate and a 4 by 2 block are then added right at the

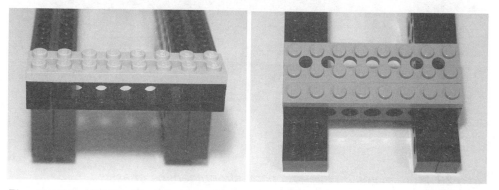

Figs.5.25 and 5.26 Beams and plates join the side pieces at both ends

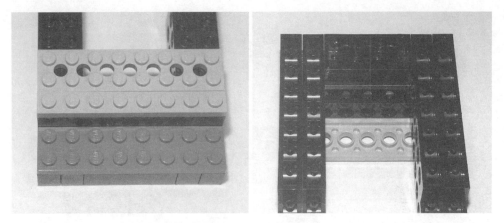

*Figs.5.27 and 5.28 A further plate and a block strengthen the front
of the chassis*

front of the chassis (Figures 5.27 and 5.28).   The chassis is then further
strengthened by adding three 8 x 2 plates and five 8 x 1 plates on the underside
(Figure 5.29). Again, the 8 by 2 plate near the front must be a type fitted with
holes so that it can accommodate the front wheel assembly.

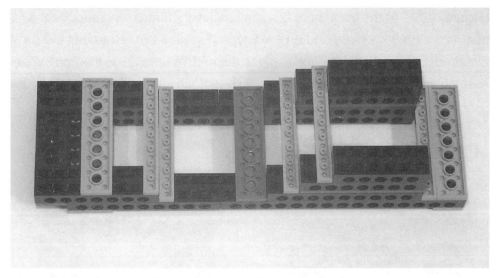

Fig.5.29 More plates on the underside strengthen the chassis

Step 3 (Figures 5.30 and 5.31)

Fig.5.30 *The parts for one assembly*

With construction of the chassis completed the rear wheels are added. The parts required for one rear wheel assembly are shown in Figure 5.30, and an identical set of parts is, of course, required for the other assembly. Begin by placing a fixing "nut" at one end of a 63-millimetre shaft, and then add a 50-millimetre diameter wheel (including the tyre) next to this. The concave side of the wheel should be towards the fixing "nut", and should partially enclose it.

Another fixing "nut" is fitted on the shaft on the other side of the wheel, and then a 40-tooth gearwheel is fitted next to this. The assembly is then fitted into the middle holes in a pair of 6 by 1 beams at the rear of the chassis. Repeat this process for the other rear wheel assembly on the other side of the chassis.

Fig.5.31 *The rear wheels in position*

Step 4 (Figures 5.32 and 5.33)

Fig.5.32 *The parts for the intermediate drive shaft*

The two intermediate drive shafts are fitted next. Figure 5.32 shows the parts required. Start by placing a 39-millimetre shaft into the top set of holes in the chassis directly above one of the rear wheels. Fit a 24-tooth

Fig.5.33 The two drive shafts installed

gearwheel on the outer end of the shaft, making sure it engages properly with the 40-tooth gearwheel on the rear wheel assembly. Then add a fixing "nut" at the other end of the shaft to keep everything in place. Repeat this process on the other side of the chassis.

Fig.5.34 The parts for the front wheel assembly

Fig.5.35 The assembly ready for installation

Step 5 (Figures 5.34 to 5.36)

The chassis is now ready for the front wheel assembly to be added. The parts required are shown in Figure 5.34. Start by fitting a 30-millimetre diameter wheel (including the tyre) near the end of a 47-millimetre long shaft. Then fit a 12-tooth bevel gearwheel onto the shaft next to the wheel, with the teeth facing towards the wheel. Incidentally, the two bevel gears are simply used as washers, and there is no drive to the front wheels. Next the shaft assembly is fitted into the right-angle bracket, and then the second bevel gear and small wheel are added. Make sure that that everything is kept loose enough so that the shaft is free to rotate easily. To complete the assembly a fixing "nut" is placed at the end of the longer (79-millimetre) shaft and the shaft is then threaded into the outer hole in the right-angle bracket. Another fixing "nut" and the smallest size of pulley are then added on the shaft to secure it to the bracket. The shaft is then fitted into the middle holes in the 8 by 2 plates at the front of the chassis and

Fig.5.36 The front wheels installed on the chassis

another "nut" is added at the top of the shaft to keep it in place. Again, make sure that everything is slightly loose so that the shaft and wheel assembly are free to rotate.

Step 6 (Figures 5.37 to 5.39)

The mounting pad for the motor consists of two 8 by 2 plates, two 2 by 2 plates, and one 8 by 1 type. These are mounted towards the rear of the chassis (Figure 5.37). Next the motors are fitted onto the mounting pads. The parts required are shown in Figure 5.38. First a 12-tooth gearwheel is fitted onto each motor, and then the motors are

Fig.5.37 The mounting pad for the motors

mounted on the chassis immediately above the rear wheels. The two 4 x 2 plates are then added onto the tops of the motors so that they hold the two motors together. This gives the finished assembly of Figure 5.39.

Fig.5.38 *The parts for the motor assembly*

Fig.5.39 *The motors installed on the chassis*

Fig.5.40 *The RCX unit's mounting pad*

Step 7 (Figures 5.40 to 5.42)

The mounting pad for the RCX unit consists of three 6 by 2 plates and an 8 x 2 type fitted on top of the chassis, in front of the motor assembly (Figure 5.40). To complete the robot the RCX unit is fitted on top of its mounting pad, immediately in front of the motor assembly, and outputs A and C of the RCX unit are connected to the motors (Figure 5.41). This completes the basic robot (Figure 5.42), which is then ready for the sensors to be fitted.

Fig.5.41 *The connections to the RCX unit*

Fig.5.42 The basic robot ready for the sensors to be installed

Adding the sensors

As pointed out previously, there are three positions on the robot for the sensors, which are the front platform, the rear platform, and underneath the midsection. The midsection is probably the best option for line following, but the sensor assembly described here

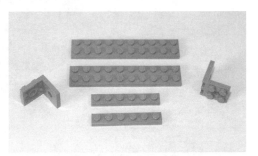

Fig.5.43 The parts for the sensors' mounting bracket

can be used in any of the three positions if you would like to experiment. The parts required are shown in Figure 5.43. The two 4 by 2 right-angle plates are

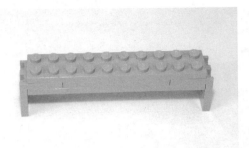

Fig.5.44 The sensor mounting bracket

fitted at opposite ends of a 10 by 2 plate. Then the two 6 by 1 plates are added on top of the 10 by 2 plate, filling in the area between the two right-angle plates. Finally, the second 10 by 2 plate is added on top of the assembly to firmly trap the right-angle plates in position, giving the finished unit of Figure 5.44.

The complete assembly is then fitted onto the robot and the sensors are wired to inputs 1 and 3 of the RCX unit. The light sensors, whether home constructed or the "real thing", will readily fit onto the right-angle plates (Figures

Fig.5.45 A home constructed light sensor fitted on the mounting bracket

Fig.5.46 A Lego light sensor fitted on the mounting bracket

5.45 and 5.46). The Lego light sensor and the home-made type that uses a phototransistor are both capable of detecting a line at a range of 25 millimetres or more. However, the line seems to be detected more quickly at closer ranges, so it is advisable to mount the light sensors so that they are quite close to the ground. This minimises tracking problems with the robot overshooting the line before a course correction can be made.

20/20bot

With its stereo vision, this robot, which we will name 20/20bot, is capable of following a line with good speed and tracking performance. The RCX code program of Figure 5.47 enables a black line on a light background to be followed. The test track provided with the Robotics Invention System is suitable for use with this software, but it is more interesting if you can make your own version on a larger piece of paper with a more tortuous track. The line needs to be fairly wide, and about 25 millimetres (as used on the Lego test track) is the minimum size that is likely to give good results. In order to be sure that the software will work properly, the robot must be positioned with the light sensors on opposite sides of the track before it is started running.

The main program sets both motors to go forward, switches on both motors, and then sets the power level at 5. 20/20bot is quite a large robot for the Lego track, and at the maximum power level of 8 it also goes quite fast. This makes it difficult for 20/20bot to negotiate the tight curves of the track, and to give it a better chance the power level is reduced to 5. This is not to say that it will crawl around the track, and it will still move faster than some rover style robots going at full throttle. Separate sensor watchers are used to monitor the two sensors.

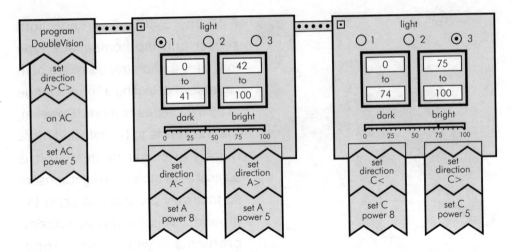

Fig.5.47 The RCX code for following a black line

First we will consider the block that monitors input 1, which is the input used for the sensor on the left-hand side of the robot. Normally a bright light level will be detected, causing both motors to be set for forward operation at a power level of 5. In other words, the robot moves forwards normally. A dark level is detected when the sensor goes over the line, and the direction of motor A is then reversed. This turns 20/20bot to the left, moving it away from the line again. The power level on motor A is increased to maximum during the turn, which helps 20/20bot to turn more sharply and reduces problems with the line being overshot.

The other sensor watcher uses a similar routine with the sensor on the right-hand side of 20/20bot. When a dark light level is detected it is motor C that is reversed and has its power level increased to maximum. This turns the robot to the right, taking it away from the line. The threshold levels used for the two sensors are very different at 41/42 for sensor 1 and 74/75 for sensor 3. This is due to the fact that sensor 1 is a genuine Lego light sensor on the prototype, whereas sensor 3 is a home-made sensor.

As always with this type of thing, you must use the RCX unit's display and the View facility to monitor the readings from both sensors when they are over the light area of the track and over the black line. From the readings you can determine a good threshold level for each sensor. Something about half way between each pair of readings should give good results. These threshold levels must be used in the program in place of the examples shown in Figure 5.47.

VB software

This listing is a Visual BASIC program that utilizes Spirit.OCX, and is functionally the same as the RCX code program for 20/20bot:

```
Private Sub Command1_Click()
With Spirit1
.InitComm
.SelectPrgm 4
.BeginOfTask 0
.SetSensorType 0, 3
.SetSensorMode 0, 4, 0
.SetSensorType 2, 3
.SetSensorMode 2, 4, 0
.On "02"
.SetFwd "02"
.SetPower "02", 2, 4
.Loop 2, 0
.If 9, 0, 1, 2, 42
.SetRwd "0"
.SetPower "0", 2, 7
.Else
.SetFwd "0"
```

```
.SetPower "0", 2, 4

.EndIf

.If 9, 2, 1, 2, 74

.SetRwd "2"

.SetPower "2", 2, 7

.Else

.SetFwd "2"

.SetPower "2", 2, 4

.EndIf

.EndLoop

.EndOfTask

End With

End Sub


Private Sub Command2_Click()

Spirit1.CloseComm

End

End Sub
```

In addition to Spirit.OCX, the form must be equipped with a command button captioned DOWNLOAD and another captioned END. These are Command1 and Command2 respectively in the program listing. To download the software to the RCX unit, first make sure that the RCX unit is switched on and is within range of the infrared tower. Then select Start from the Run menu and operate the DOWLOAD button when the program window appears. Downloading has finished once the light on the tower has gone out, and the END button is then operated to terminate the program and return to Visual BASIC.

The program starts by initialising communication with the infrared tower, and selecting program 4, which is program 5 in the 1 to 5 numbering system used by the RCX unit. The main program is entered, and this is the only task. This starts by setting inputs 0 and 2 (labelled 1 and 3 on the RCX unit) to operate with light sensors in the percentage mode. Then both motors are switched on, set to go forward, and the power level is set at 4, which is just over half power in the 0 to 7 method of power control.

Next the program goes into an infinite loop that repeatedly checks the sensors and makes any necessary changes to the output settings. First an If instruction tests the sensor on input 0, and it performs the next two commands if the value returned from the sensor is less than the constant value 42. In other words, it performs these commands if the sensor is over the black line. If this condition is met, motor 0 is set into reverse and its power level is increased to maximum (level 7). If the sensor is not over the line the two instructions after the Else command will be performed instead. These set motor 0 to go forward at a power level of 4, which means that normal operation is provided. This If...Then...Else structure takes the place of the first sensor watcher in the version of the program written in RCX code. A similar If..Then...Else structure takes the place of the second sensor watcher. This one is essentially the same, but monitors input 2 and controls motor 2.

Most programs that provide line following using a single sensor have a few conditions that have to be met in the "fine print". For example, the robot may have to go around the track in a certain direction, or it may only be able to follow the inside edge of the line. Using two sensors eliminates restrictions such as these. 20/20bot will happily follow the black line in either direction, and it will not be fazed if the line twists and turns all over the place. Neither of the programs will enable 20/20bot to follow a white line on a dark background, but little modification should be needed to provide tracking of a white line. I have not tried it in practice, but the RCX code program of Figure 5.48 should provide this function. It is just a matter of having each motor run forwards when its sensor detects a low light level, and in reverse when a high light level is detected, instead of the other way around.

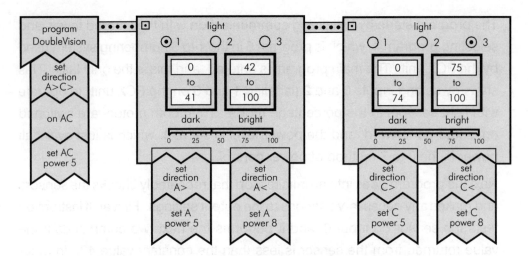

Fig.5.48 The RCX code for following a light line on a dark background

Findbot

20/20bot is good at tracking a black line, but it will only work if it is positioned with the sensors on either side of the line before the Run button is operated. It is not difficult to modify the software so that the robot moves forward until it finds a line, and then locks onto that line and tracks it. The Visual BASIC program listed here provides this action:

```
Private Sub Command1_Click()

With Spirit1

.InitComm

.SelectPrgm 3

.BeginOfTask 0

.SetSensorType 0, 3

.SetSensorMode 0, 4, 0

.SetSensorType 2, 3
```

```
.SetSensorMode 2, 4, 0

.On "02"

.SetFwd "02"

.SetPower "02", 2, 4

.While 9, 0, 0, 2, 42

.EndWhile

.While 9, 0, 1, 2, 42

.SetRwd "0"

.SetPower "0", 2, 7

.EndWhile

.SetFwd "0"

.SetPower "0", 2, 4

.Loop 2, 0

.If 9, 0, 1, 2, 42

.SetRwd "0"

.SetPower "0", 2, 7

.Else

.SetFwd "0"

.SetPower "0", 2, 4

.EndIf

.If 9, 2, 1, 2, 74

.SetRwd "2"

.SetPower "2", 2, 7

.Else
```

```
.SetFwd "2"

.SetPower "2", 2, 4

.EndIf

.EndLoop

.EndOfTask

End With

End Sub


Private Sub Command2_Click()

Spirit1.CloseComm

End

End Sub
```

This is much the same as the original program, but there is an additional routine ahead of the infinite loop that provides the line tracking. The first While instruction does nothing until the light reading from sensor 0 is less than 42. In other words, Findbot keeps going forward until sensor 0 is over the black line. The second While loop then turns the robot and keeps it turning until sensor 0 is off the line again. This manoeuvres Findbot so that there is one sensor on each side of the line, and the original infinite loop then takes over and provides line tracking, as before. The program could be refined still further to make the robot go through a search pattern until it finds the line, and there is plenty of scope for experimentation here.

Slow response

The response times of photodiodes and phototransistors are quite fast, which contrasts with much slower response times of cadmium sulphide cells. The attack time of a cadmium sulphide cell is slower than that of a semiconductor photocell, but a typical cell is still quite fast in this respect. It normally takes no more than a few milliseconds for the cell to respond to a large increase in light level. The decay times tend to be much longer though, and it can take a few seconds for a cadmium sulphide photocell to fully respond to a large reduction in light level. This relative slowness and memory effect with high light levels is normally considered a drawback, but it is potentially useful. The speed of a semiconductor light sensor plus the method of periodic sampling used by the RCX unit make the chances of catching a short burst of light very slim. One way around the problem is to use some extra electronics to hold any change in the output voltage for several milliseconds so that the RCX unit has a chance to sample the changed level. Simply using a cadmium sulphide has much the same effect though, with the slow decay time holding any change in output voltage for at least several milliseconds. This gives the RCX unit more than ample time to measure the changed reading and respond accordingly.

Camerashybot

The joke robot featured here responds to the pulse of light from the flashgun of a camera. The basic premise is that the robot is camera shy, and if you take its photograph using flash light it gives three squeaks of surprise, turns around and then runs off and hides! This sort of thing usually amuses and impresses family and friends. In a world where technology is increasingly taken for granted, if you come up with something like a Lego robot that builds more robots you will probably fail to impress. Show

Fig.5.49 Camerashybot requires a single cadmium sulphide light sensor

Fig.5.50 The parts for one of the "eye" assemblies

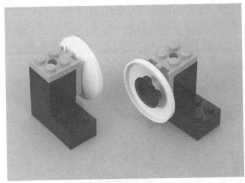

Fig.5.51 The two "eye" assemblies

Fig.5.52 Camerashybot equipped with two dummy eyes

someone the camera shy robot you have just built and they will probably tell everyone all about it.

Camerashybot is just the standard rover robot with a cadmium sulphide photocell mounted at the front and connected to input 2 of the RCX unit (Figure 5.49). No LED is required in this case, so just a simple sensor consisting of the photocell mounted in a brick will suffice. Note that the Lego light sensor will not work in this application, and neither will the home-made phototransistor based light sensor described previously. Although one might expect the pulse of light to be picked up occasionally by the RCX unit's sampling system, despite numerous attempts I never managed to get any response using a sensor based on a phototransistor.

The Robotics Invention System includes parts that enable "eyes" to be fitted to robots so that they look more animal like, and fitting a couple of these should enhance the comic effect. The parts need for one eye assembly are shown in Figure 5.50, and Figure 5.51 shows the two completed assemblies. Two 2 by 2 bricks are fitted one on top of the other, and then they are mounted at one end on a 4 by 2 brick. A 4 by 2 right-angle plate is then mounted on top of this assembly. The black eye component is fitted onto the white dish-like piece, and then these are mounted on the right-angle plate. The second eye assembly is then constructed in much the same way, but note that the second one is a "mirror image" of the first eye assembly. The finished units are mounted on the front platform of the robot (Figure 5.52).

This is the Visual BASIC listing for Camerashybot:

```
Private Sub Command1_Click()

With Spirit1

.InitComm

.SelectPrgm 2

.BeginOfTask 0

.SetSensorType 1, 1

.SetSensorMode 1, 0, 0

.SetVar 1, 9, 1

.SubVar 1, 2, 100

.Loop 2, 0

.If 9, 1, 1, 0, 1

.On "02"

.SetFwd "2"

.SetRwd "0"

.Wait 2, 70

.SetFwd "0"

.PlayTone 1500, 10

.Wait 2, 30
```

```
              .PlayTone 1500, 10

              .Wait 2, 30

              .PlayTone 1500, 10

              .Wait 2, 350

              .PlayTone 1500, 10

              .Wait 2, 30

              .PlayTone 1500, 10

              .SetRwd "0"

              .Wait 2, 35

              .SetFwd "0"

              .Wait 2, 200

              .Off "02"

              .StopAllTasks

              .EndIf

              .EndLoop

              .EndOfTask

          End With

          End Sub


          Private Sub Command2_Click()

          Spirit1.CloseComm

          End

          End Sub
```

The first part of the program initialises communication with the infrared tower, selects a program number, and sets the sensor type and mode. The sensor is a passive (switch) type that is used in raw mode. Next the program reads the value from sensor 1 (input 2 in RCX terminology) and places it in variable 1. The value stored in variable 1 is then reduced by 100 using a SubVar instruction. Normally there is a problem with the ambient light level when using a light sensor. Simply having the software perform a task when a certain light level is exceeded can not be guaranteed to give the desired result, because the ambient light level might sometimes exceed the threshold level. Setting the threshold level very high could cure this problem, but could make the system so insensitive that it often fails to work.

One way around the problem, and the one used here, is to take an initial light reading and store the result. The software then checks the light sensor periodically, and checks whether or not it has changed by more than a certain amount relative to the initial reading. Here we are looking for a light reading that has reduced by more than 100, and it is for this reason that 100 is deducted from the value stored in the variable. It might seem that 100 should be added to this value, but remember that in raw mode higher light values give reduced readings.

Next the program goes into an indefinite loop. An If instruction compares the reading from the light sensor with the value stored in variable 1, and a string of instructions are performed if the current reading is less than the modified initial reading in variable 1. This condition should be met when the flashgun is fired, and the string of commands is then performed. First one motor is set to go forward and the other is set to reverse, and a Wait instruction maintains this state for 0.7 seconds. This gets Camerashybot to turn through about 180 degrees, after which both motors are set to forward operation. Then a series of three Wait and PlayTone instructions produce the three squeaking sounds.

Next a Wait instruction provides a pause of 3.5 seconds, during which the robot continues to move away from the camera and make its escape. Two further PlayTone instructions and a Wait type then provide two more squeaks, and then one motor is placed in reverse for 0.35 seconds. This turns Camerashybot through approximately 90 degrees. The motor is returned to forward operation and then a further Wait instruction keeps the robot going forward for a further two seconds. Finally, the motors are switched off and a StopAllTasks halts the program.

The instructions provided after the If command are really intended for guidance only. To get the best effect the string of instructions should be designed to get Camerashybot to run away from the camera and hide under a table, or something of this type. The robot does not know where it is going or what it is doing, but it must look as though it does. It aids the effect if the robot does one or two quick spins in panic on its way.

Showing off Camerashybot to your family and friends could waste a lot of film, but many cameras can fire their flashguns without any film in the camera. A digital camera is ideal for this sort of thing, since it enables you to snap away merrily with no film to worry about.

Slope version

The use of Boolean mode with a slope value of other than zero gives the sort of light detection that is well suited to an application such as Camerashybot. The absolute light level and slow changes in level are of no interest, but we do require the robot to be triggered by a sudden change in the light level. This is exactly what is provided if the slope feature is implemented. This is a modified version of the Camerashybot software that utilizes the slope feature:

```
Private Sub Command1_Click()
With Spirit1
.InitComm
.SelectPrgm 3
.BeginOfTask 0
```

```
.SetSensorType 1, 1

.SetSensorMode 1, 1, 30

.Loop 2, 0

.If 9, 1, 2, 2, 1

.On "02"

.SetFwd "2"

.SetRwd "0"

.Wait 2, 70

.SetFwd "0"

.PlayTone 1500, 10

.Wait 2, 30

.PlayTone 1500, 10

.Wait 2, 30

.PlayTone 1500, 10

.Wait 2, 350

.PlayTone 1500, 10

.Wait 2, 30

.PlayTone 1500, 10

.SetRwd "0"

.Wait 2, 35

.SetFwd "0"

.Wait 2, 200

.Off "02"

.StopAllTasks
```

```
.EndIf

.EndLoop

.EndOfTask

End With

End Sub


Private Sub Command2_Click()

Spirit1.CloseComm

End

End Sub
```

One change in this version is that an initial reading is no longer taken and placed in a variable. Instead, the SetSensorMode command has been modified to use Boolean mode with a slope value of 30. A change in the input value of 30 is therefore needed from one reading to the next in order to toggle the Boolean value from 0 to 1. The If instruction has also been modified, and it now checks for an input level of 1. When this condition is met, the string of instructions following the If instruction are performed, and Camerashybot goes through its routine. In practice the slope option seems to work very well. This version of the software works over a wide range of ambient light levels, is not bothered by slow changes in the light level, but is very sensitive to the flashes of light from the flashgun.

Sound sensing

Motor noise

There is no Lego sound sensor, but building a sound sensor is not difficult. It is only fair to point out straight away that there is a major problem in using a sensor of this type. A sound sensor works fine when the robot is not active, but as soon as the motors start to operate there will inevitably be a large amount of noise and vibration. The noise level may not actually be all that high and this obviously depends on the particular robot in use. However, the microphone will inevitably be quite close to the motors and other moving parts. Even if the sensor is not particularly sensitive, this close proximity to the sound source tends to make the mechanical noise of the robot overwhelm other sounds.

Probably of greater relevance, the fact that the microphone is mounted on the robot results in a direct mechanical link from moving parts to the microphone. Unfortunately, there is no easy way around this problem. It is possible to reduce the amount of noise and vibration picked up from the moving parts, but it is unlikely that the problem could be reduced to a satisfactory level. There are electronic means for counteracting the noise, but it is again unlikely that any easy way of defeating the problem could be devised.

This is not to say that a sound sensor is of no practical use. With persistence it might actually be possible to produce a sensor that could hear your commands through the mechanical noise of the robot. The more practical approach is to use a simple sensor, but to only utilize it when the robot is stationary. One sure-fire method of impressing your family and friends is to have a robot that brings you a chocolate bar when you clap your hands.

Fig.6.1 The block diagram for the sound sensor

When you clap your hands again the robot returns from whence it came. Of course, everything has to be carefully set up in advance for this to work properly. The robot is hidden somewhere out of sight, such as under a chair or cupboard unit. The sound sensor detects the hand clap and activates the robot which then goes through a series of manoeuvres, taking it from its hiding place to your chair side. Although the robot then stops, the program is still running

Once you have taken the chocolate bar you clap your hands, triggering the robot into operation once again. It then goes through another carefully calculated series of manoeuvres that take it back to its hiding place. The robot then shuts itself down so that it cannot be spuriously operated by any sounds that occur thereafter. When using this type of sensor you have to bear in mind that the robot will respond to any loud sound, and not just to a particular type of sound.

Sensor operation

The block diagram of Figure 6.1 shows the general scheme of things used for this sensor. The output signal from any normal microphone is quite small, and even with loud sounds it is unlikely to be more than a few millivolts. The first stage of the sensor therefore amplifies the signal from the microphone to a more usable level. A high degree of amplification could be used to provide the sensor with excellent sensitivity, but this would probably be a mistake. As already pointed out, the sensor has no way of distinguishing your commands from any other sounds in the vicinity. The robot will respond to every little sound if a large amount of amplification is used, rendering the sensor unusable. A modest amount of amplification gives quite low sensitivity, and quite loud sounds such as hand claps are then needed in order to activate the robot. On the other hand, your robot waiter will not keep popping out with the chocolate bar ahead of schedule.

The output from the amplifier is a varying DC voltage that reaches a maximum on positive signal peaks and a minimum on negative signal peaks. We require a DC voltage that rises and falls in sympathy with the average sound level. Such a voltage can be read by an input of the RCX unit where high readings will indicate the presence of loud sounds. The conversion is achieved by feeding the amplified audio signal through a rectifier that removes the negative half cycles but allows the positive half cycles to pass. A smoothing circuit removes the rapid changes in the signal voltage to give the required DC voltage that rises and falls in sympathy with the audio signal level. This voltage receives a small amount of amplification, but the main purpose of the output amplifier is to act as a buffer stage that can properly drive an input of the RCX unit.

Circuit operation

The full circuit diagram for the sound sensor appears in Figure 6.2. The left-hand section of the circuit is the usual diode array that provides the supply voltage for the sensor and the diode mixing at the output. Supply smoothing capacitor C1 has a higher value than normal, and this is due to the fact that an audio circuit such as this tends to be vulnerable to noise on the supply lines. Unless the supply is reasonably noise-free it is likely that supply noise would find its way into the signal path and hold the sensor in the activated state.

The microphone (Mic1) is actually a cased ceramic resonator that is intended to operate as a sort of miniature loudspeaker in simple alarm circuits. However, it works quite well in reverse as a crude crystal microphone. The audio quality is probably pretty terrible, but this is of no consequence in an application such as this. We simply require something that is cheap, reasonably efficient, and tough. A cased ceramic resonator fulfils these requirements very well. A crystal microphone insert should work equally well, but these are less readily available than was once the case. The innards of a crystal earpiece should

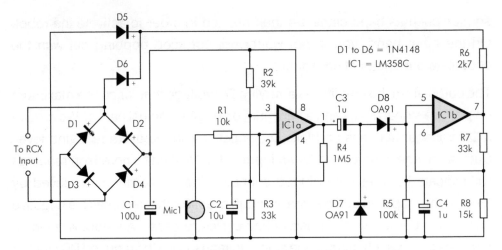

Fig.6.2 *The full circuit diagram for the sound sensor*

also do the job, but an earphone of this type is likely to be more expensive than a ceramic resonator.

Operational amplifier IC1a is used in the input amplifier, and this is a straightforward inverting mode amplifier. Resistor R1 sets the input impedance at 10k, and in conjunction with R4 the closed loop voltage gain of IC1a is set at 150 times. An input impedance of 10k is very low for an amplifier that will operate with a crystal microphone, and will give a very poor low frequency response. This is an advantage in this case where there could be problems with spurious triggering due to the vibration caused by people walking near the robot.

C3 couples the output of IC1a to a simple half-wave rectifier based on diodes D7 and D8. The circuit will work using silicon diodes, but there is an advantage in using germanium diodes, due to their lower forward voltage drop. OA91 diodes are specified for D7 and D8, but any small germanium diodes should work equally well. Schottky diodes also have relatively low forward voltage drops and should provide a similar level of performance to germanium diodes in this circuit.

The smoothing circuit is comprised of resistor R5 and capacitor C4. The output impedance of IC1a is quite low, which gives the circuit a rapid response time. The smoothing circuit therefore responds almost immediately to any increase in the amplitude of the output signal from IC1a. The comparatively high value of R5 gives a much longer decay time. This ensures that the RCX unit's sampling system will not sample between signal peaks and miss loud sounds.

The decay time must not be too long though, since different commands can be given to the robot by clapping once or by clapping twice in rapid succession. The decay time must be short so that two sounds in rapid succession will produce two distinct output pulses from the smoothing circuit. The time constant of R5 and C4 is 0.1 seconds, and this seems to give good results in practice. IC1b is used as the DC amplifier at the output of the circuit. This is a simple non-inverting amplifier having its voltage gain set at just over three times by the negative feedback loop (R7 and R8).

Construction

The component layout and wiring for the stripboard are shown in Figure 6.3, with the breaks in the copper strips shown separately in Figure 6.4. Construction of the board follows along the normal lines. Although this board is slightly more complex than the ones used in the two light sensors described in chapter 5, it is probably no more difficult to build. With more components and a bigger board there are more opportunities for errors to creep in, but construction is eased somewhat because the components are less crammed together.

The LM358C used for IC1 is not sensitive to static charges and does not require any special handling precautions. Nevertheless, it is still a good idea to use a holder for all DIL (dual in-line) integrated circuits. This avoids the possibility of overheating the component when soldering it to the board, since it is the holder that is soldered to the board. The integrated circuit plugs into the holder once all the connections have been completed. The pins of IC1 will probably have to be pressed inwards slightly before it will fit into the holder.

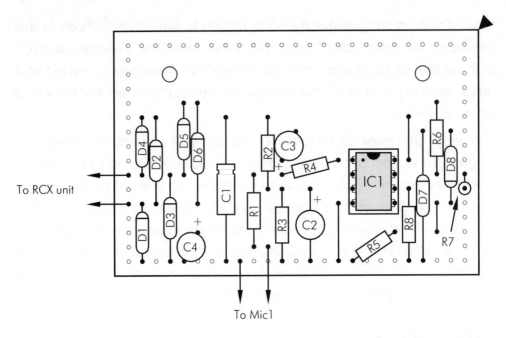

Fig.6.3 The component layout for the sound sensor board

The end of the component that has pin 1 is usually indicated by a small dimple and (or) a notch at that end of the body. The notch or dimple should be at the top, as viewed in Figure 6.3. These days some integrated circuits have a line marked across the body next to pin 1, and again, this end of the component should be towards the top as viewed in Figure 6.3. One advantage of using a holder is that the component is easily removed if you should accidentally fit it around the wrong way. Carefully prise it free using the blade of a small screwdriver. Simply pulling an integrated circuit from its holder by hand is not a good idea, because it tends to skew as it comes free. This bends the pins and could seriously damage them. The pins could also bury themselves in one of your fingers.

Diodes D7 and D8 are germanium components, and these are less tolerant of heat than the more common silicon components. There is a little gadget called a heat-shunt that can be clipped onto a lead to remove heat while soldered connections are being made, but it is not essential to use one of these. These two diodes should be safe provided the soldered joints are completed reasonably quickly. They should be the last components to be fitted to the circuit board. Figure 6.5 shows the component side view of the finished board, and the underside of the board is shown in Figure 6.6.

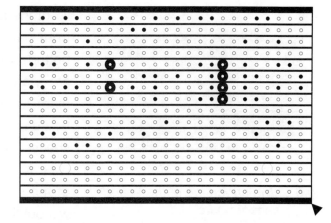

Fig.6.4 The underside view of the circuit board

Case

The two light sensor circuit boards are small and a tight fit in their cases, making it unnecessary to bolt the boards in place. This board is somewhat larger and it does require a couple of mounting bolts. The two mounting holes in the board are 3 millimetres in diameter and will accept either 6BA or metric M2.5 screws. A Lego battery box is sometimes used for larger home-built sensors and might be suitable for this project, but it is a relatively expensive

Fig.6.5 The completed sound sensor board

solution. For a larger sensor such as this it is probably best to abandon the use of Lego bricks or other parts for the case and use a conventional plastic enclosure.

The board is designed to fit a box that measures 75 by 56 by 25 millimetres, but any box of about this size or a little larger should suffice. The removable

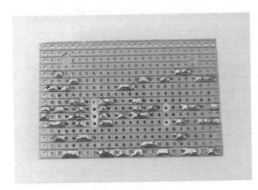

Fig.6.6 The underside of the sound sensor board

lid of the case is used here as the front panel. The circuit board is bolted in place at the rear of the case, and it is essential to use an extra mounting nut between the board and the case to act as a short spacer. The underside of the board is far from flat due to the presence of the soldered connections, and without the extra nut the board, and possibly the case as well, will buckle

as the mounting nuts are tightened. This may not cause any damage, but there is a real possibility that the board will crack or even shatter. Using extra mounting nuts or very short spacers avoids this possibility.

The ceramic resonator is mounted on the front panel. These components are available in plain and cased versions, but I would only recommend using the cased version in this application. The mounting arrangements for these components vary somewhat from one make to another, but most are bolted in place using a couple of small bolts. The built-in mounting holes are usually for 8BA or metric M2 screws, which are not normally supplied with the resonator incidentally. It is possible to mount the resonator on the front or rear surface of the panel. Mounting it on the front surface is easier because you only have to drill two holes for the mounting bolts, plus a third hole to permit the two leads to pass through to the interior of the case.

Things are neater if the resonator is mounted on the rear surface, and this avoids the need for the small hole for the two leads. Instead, a large hole to take the body of the component is required. Cutting a hole of this size in such a small panel is awkward and will seriously weaken the panel, but it can be done using a chassis punch, coping saw, or any of the other standard methods. The two leads of a ceramic resonator are usually coloured red and black, but strictly speaking this is not a form of polarised component, and in this application the leads can certainly be connected to the board either way around.

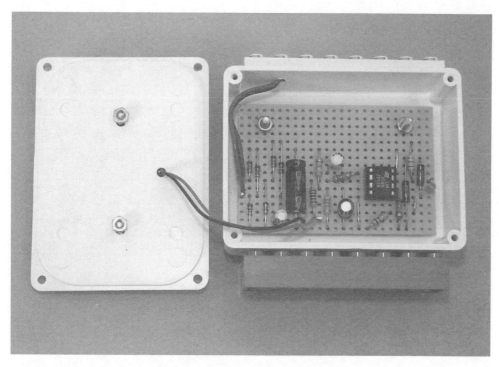

Fig.6.7 Interior view of the completed sound sensor

It is possible to connect the circuit board to the RCX unit using the same method that was adopted for the two light sensors. However, a connector plate is well suited to larger sensors such is this, and this is the method used on the prototype. A twin lead about 30 millimetres or so in length is connected to the two metal strips on the underside of the connector plate, well towards one end. A hole for this lead is drilled in the top panel of the case well towards the right-hand side of the unit.

The lead is then threaded through the hole in the case and the plate is glued in place on top of the case. Due to the far from flat underside of the plate it is essential to use an adhesive that has good gap-filling capability. An epoxy adhesive should do the job quite well, but a glue-gun provides the quickest and easiest way of fixing the plate to the case. A 6 by 2 or 8 by 2 brick is glued to the underside of the case to provide a means of mounting the sensor on the case. Again, an adhesive that has good gap-filling properties is essential.

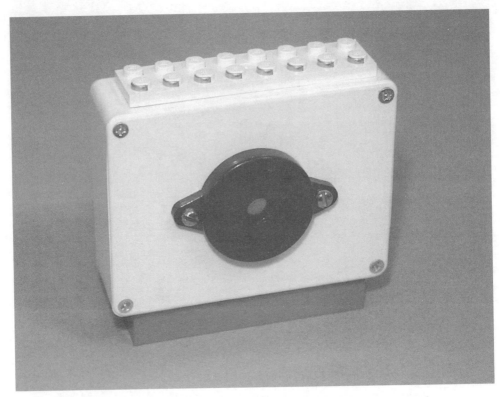

Figure 6.8 The finished sound sensor, ready to be fitted on a robot

To complete the sensor the twin lead from the connector plate and the two leads from the ceramic resonator are connected to the appropriate pins on the circuit board. Figure 6.7 shows an interior view of the finished sensor and Figure 6.8 shows an exterior view. The sensor will fit onto the front platform of the rover vehicle immediately in front of the RCX unit, or on the rear platform. It is connected to input 1 of the RCX unit using an ordinary Lego lead. The lead can be connected to any group of four terminals on the sensor's connector plate, and with any orientation.

The View facility can be used to check that the sensor is functioning. With the input set up for operation with a light sensor, a very high reading should be obtained under standby conditions. A reading of around 90 is obtained using the prototype sensor, but the reading will probably vary somewhat from one sensor to another. Blowing on the microphone should send the reading to a very low level, and it will probably go right down to zero. Switch off the RCX unit at once and recheck the entire wiring, etc., if there is any sign of a malfunction.

Although the microphone is what would normally be considered omni-directional, the sensor is to some extent directional, and it is more sensitive to sounds that emanate in front of the sensor. Ideally two sensors would be used,

Fig.6.9 The completed robot, ready to make deliveries

one on the rear facing backward and one at the front facing forward. In practice though, a single sensor should give good results, especially when the sensor is used indoors. Sounds reflected from the walls, ceiling, etc., then help to provide a route from the source to the sensor.

The prototype rover robot was set up for chocolate deliveries by having the sensor mounted immediately in front of the RCX unit, and installing the two "eyes" (Figure 6.9). Additionally, a holder for the chocolate bar was added on the rear platform. The holder is based on two 10 by 1 beams and two 4 by 1 beams. The beams have 10 by 1 and 6 by 1 plates fitted on the upper

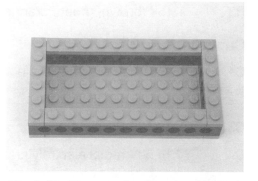

Fig.6.10 The tray for the chocolate bar

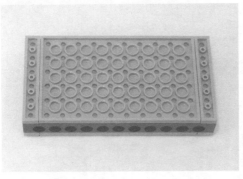

side (Figure 6.10). They are joined on the underside using a 10 by 6 plate and two 6 by 1 types (Figure 6.11). This assembly is then fitted on the rear platform of the robot, immediately behind the motors (Figure 6.12).

Fig.6.11 The underside of the tray

Components list

Resistors, all 0.25 watt 5% carbon film

R1	10k (brown, black, orange, gold)
R2	39k (orange, white, orange, gold)
R3	33k (orange, orange, orange, gold)
R4	1M5 (brown, green, green, gold)
R5	100k (brown, black, yellow, gold)
R6	2k7 (red, violet, red, gold)
R7	33k (orange, orange, orange, gold)
R8	15k (brown, green, orange, gold)

Capacitors

C1	100μ 10V axial or PC electrolytic
C2	10μ 25V PC electrolytic
C3	1μ 50V PC electrolytic
C4	1μ 50V radial electrolytic

Semiconductors

IC1	LM358C or LM358N

D1 to D6   1N4148 (6 off)

D7   OA91

D8   OA91

Miscellaneous

Mic1   Cased ceramic resonator

Plastic box about 75 by 56 by 25 millimetres

0.1-inch pitch stripboard having 25 holes by 16 copper strips

8-pin DIL holder for IC1

8 by 2 connector plate

6BA or M2.5 fixings

6 by 2 or 8 by 2 Lego brick

Wire, solder-pins, solder, etc.

Test software

Figure 6.13 shows a simple test program for Clapbot written in RCX code. The program starts by simply waiting for one second, and this avoids having the unit instantly triggered by any vibration caused as you press the Run button. The program then goes into an indefinite loop that starts with another one-second delay. This one serves no purpose on the first run through the loop routine, but on subsequent

Fig.6.12 *The tray fitted on the rear platform of the robot*

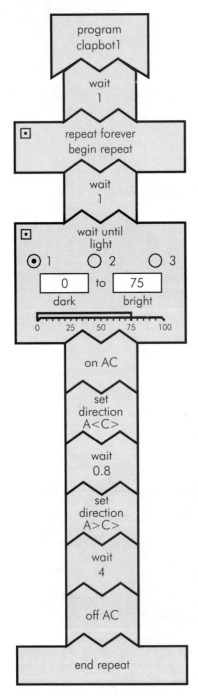

program
clapbot1

wait
1

repeat forever
begin repeat

wait
1

wait until
light

● 1   ○ 2   ○ 3

0   to   75

dark   bright

0   25   50   75   100

on AC

set
direction
A<C>

wait
0.8

set
direction
A>C>

wait
4

off AC

end repeat

Fig.6.13 The RCX code test program

occasions it gives the sensor time to recover from any noise picked up from the motors. This avoids having the robot continually retriggering itself. Next a wait until block monitors the sensors and blocks the progress of the program until a suitably low reading is obtained. Obviously there is no sound sensor option, because there is no Lego sound sensor. This block is intended for monitoring a light sensor, which gives more or less the right attributes for the present application. It sets the RCX unit to provide power to the sensor, and the input operates in percentage mode.

The use of percentage mode means that higher output levels from the sensor give lower readings from the port. Under standby conditions the reading from the port is quite high at around 90. This block waits for an input of 75 or less before it moves the program on to the next block, and any reasonably loud sound should give a reading in this range.

Once the program moves beyond the wait until block a series of instructions get the robot to turn through about 180 degrees, move forward for three seconds, and then stop. At this point the program returns to the beginning of the loop where it waits one second, and then waits once more for a suitable reading from the sound sensor. If you try running this program, clapping your hands should result in Clapbot turning around and moving away for three seconds. If you clap your hands again it will turn around and return to its starting position. It will continue with this routine for as long as you keep clapping.

If you prefer to use Visual BASIC and Spirit.OCX, this simple program provides the same basic action as the test routine in RCX code:

```
Private Sub Command1_Click()
With Spirit1
.InitComm
.SelectPrgm 2
.BeginOfTask 0
.SetSensorType 1, 3
.Loop 2, 0
.Wait 2, 100
.While 9, 0, 0, 2, 75
.EndWhile
.On "02"
.SetRwd "0"
.SetFwd "2"
.Wait 2, 80
.SetFwd "0"
.Wait 2, 300
.Off "02"
.EndLoop
.EndOfTask
```

```
End With

End Sub


Private Sub Command2_Click()

Spirit1.CloseComm

End

End Sub
```

This program works in much the same way as the RCX code version. The wait until block of the RCX code program has been replaced with an empty While...EndWhile loop that provides the same function. In other respects the Visual BASIC program is a direct equivalent to the original.

Waiter service

The RCX code program of Figure 6.14 gets Clapbot to provide the basic chocolate bar delivery service. The program is shown in two sections in Figure 6.14 because it is too long to fit the page in one piece. It is, of course, entered as one long column of commands on the screen. The program operates in a similar fashion to the basic test program, but it is not an infinite loop and the robot is effectively deactivated when the end of the program is reached. Also, there are two wait until blocks. The first of these provides the initial hold-off that prevents Clapbot from exiting its hiding place until you clap you hands. The second comes into action once the initial routine has been completed and the chocolate bar has been delivered.

Obviously the routine that follows each wait until block must be tailored to suit the route that Clapbot must take. The example instructions move the robot forward for two seconds, and then forwards for a further five seconds after a 90-degree turn to the right. The second routine gets Clapbot to turn around, and then it retraces its "steps". Expect to undertake a fair amount of experimentation before Clapbot follows your chosen route with adequate

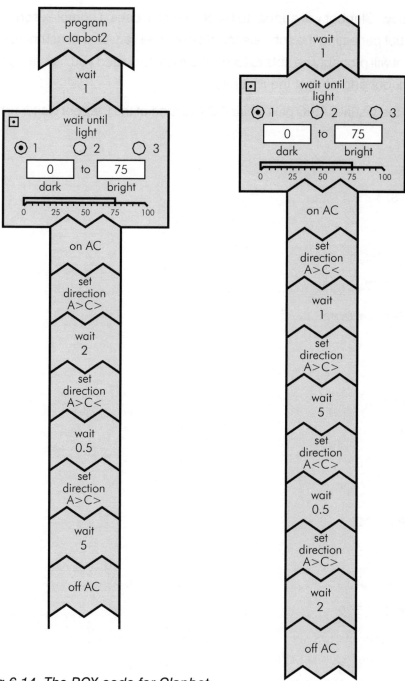

Fig.6.14 The RCX code for Clapbot

accuracy. Clapbot will appear to be cleverer if it uses a complex sequence of turns, but perfecting the software for this could be very time consuming indeed. Clapbot will probably be able to follow the route provided you have the patience to work out and perfect the routines.

This is the Visual BASIC plus Spirit.OCX version of the Clapbot waiter program:

```
Private Sub Command1_Click()
With Spirit1
.InitComm
.SelectPrgm 3
.BeginOfTask 0
.SetSensorType 1, 3
.Wait 2, 100
.While 9, 0, 0, 2, 75
.EndWhile
.On "02"
.SetFwd "02"
.Wait 2, 200
.SetRwd "2"
.Wait 2, 50
.SetFwd "2"
.Wait 2, 500
.Off "02"
.Wait 2, 100
.While 9, 0, 0, 2, 75
```

```
.EndWhile

.On "02"

.SetFwd "0"

.SetRwd "2"

.Wait 2, 100

.SetFwd "2"

.Wait 2, 500

.SetRwd "0"

.Wait 2, 50

.SetFwd "0"

.Wait 2, 200

.Off "02"

.EndOfTask

End With

End Sub


Private Sub Command2_Click()

Spirit1.CloseComm

End

End Sub
```

This is again a straightforward translation from the original software in RCX code. An advantage of the Visual BASIC version is that the delays in the Wait instructions can be set with ten times greater precision. This should enable the course of the robot to be set with much greater precision.

Applausebot

So far we have settled for having one hand clap to issue a simple "go" command to the robot, but it is possible to have several commands available by using a different number of claps for each command. This Visual BASIC program is designed to accept two commands that are issued by clapping once or twice. Using one clap results in the robot going through a simple manoeuvre and two claps deactivates it. However, any series of commands can be used in place of the two example routines.

```
Private Sub Command1_Click()
With Spirit1
.InitComm
.SelectPrgm 0
.BeginOfTask 0
.SetSensorType 0, 3
.SetSensorMode 0, 4, 0
.Loop 2, 0
.Wait 2, 100
.While 9, 0, 0, 2, 75
.EndWhile
.Wait 2, 30
.SetVar 1, 2, 0
.If 9, 0, 1, 2, 75
.SetVar 1, 2, 1
.EndIf
.Wait 2, 10
```

```
.If 9, 0, 1, 2, 75
.SetVar 1, 2, 1
.EndIf
.Wait 2, 10
.If 9, 0, 1, 2, 75
.SetVar 1, 2, 1
.EndIf
.Wait 2, 10
.If 9, 0, 1, 2, 75
.SetVar 1, 2, 1
.EndIf
.Wait 2, 10
.If 0, 1, 2, 2, 1
.PlayTone 100, 40
.StopAllTasks
.Else
.PlayTone 1000, 40
.On "02"
.SetRwd "0"
.SetFwd "2"
.Wait 2, 80
.SetFwd "0"
.Wait 2, 300
.Off "02"
```

```
.EndIf

.EndLoop

.EndOfTask

End With

End Sub


Private Sub Command2_Click()

Spirit1.CloseComm

End

End Sub
```

If you keep clapping once, the program operates like the simple test program featured previously. The robot turns around and moves away, then turns around and returns, turns around once more and moves away, and so on. Additionally, it "beeps" briefly at a fairly high pitch of 1000 hertz (1 kilohertz). An empty While...EndWhile loop towards the beginning of the program provides a hold-off until the hand clap is detected, and the instructions near the end of the program manoeuvre the robot from one place to the other. The middle part of the program checks for a second hand clap, and brings the program to a halt if a second clap is detected.

After the first clap is detected the program waits for 0.3 seconds to give time for the reading from the sound sensor to decay. A series of four identical routines then check the reading from the sound sensor at 0.1-second intervals. This relatively low rate of checking is acceptable because a hand clap will cause an output pulse of at least 0.1 seconds in duration at the output of the sound sensor. Each of the four routines checks to see if the value returned from the sound sensor is less than 75, and sets variable 1 at a value of 1 if it is. In other words, if a clap is detected, variable 1 is set at 1.

Incidentally, variable 1 is given a starting value of 0 earlier in the program. At the end of the four checks the value in variable 1 will be 0 if no second clap was detected, or 1 if a second clap did occur. An If instruction tests the value stored in variable 1, and halts the program if it is set at 1. It also produces a low-pitched "buzz" sound so that you know the robot has been successfully deactivated. If the value in variable 1 is other than 1, the instructions after the Else command are performed, and the robot goes through its simple manoeuvre sequence. The program then loops back to the beginning and waits for another hand clap.

Coughing up

This one is definitely my idea of the ideal robot. It is a bit like a sweet vending machine, but it does not require any money. Instead, you just clap your hands and it dispenses a sweet. Better still, clap your hands two or three times and it dispenses two or three sweets. The only thing that stops Sweetiebot from being absolutely perfect is that you have to load it with sweets before it will dispense any. Sweetiebot is a bit fussy about the sweets it will dispense. These days most sweets have fancy wrappers with twisted ends, and these protruding ends tend to get stuck in Sweetiebot's "throat". It works best with square-shaped sweets having simple fold-around wrappers, such as a well-known "Fruits" sweet.

It actually makes a very good dispenser of some makes of cough sweet. These mostly have simple wrappers that avoid blockages. If you cough once it delivers one sweet. If you are a bad case and cough two or three times, Sweetiebot thoughtfully dispenses two or three cough sweets. Is this the world's first loving and caring robot? No, but if you have a cold and are feeling a bit low, Sweetiebot might cheer you up a bit anyway. Incidentally, for reasons of hygiene it is definitely not a good idea to use Sweetiebot to dispense non-wrapped sweets.

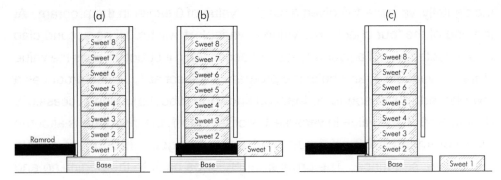

Fig.6.15 *The simple mechanism used in Sweetiebot*

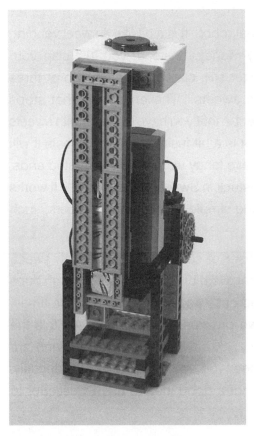

Fig.6.16 *Sweetiebot ready to dispense some sweets*

Mechanism

On the face of it, a sweet dispenser can operate on a simple trapdoor principle, with the sweets piled up on top of the trapdoor. Opening and quickly closing the door again will let through one sweet at a time. In practice it is difficult to get such a basic system to operate properly, since the timing of the door movements have to be very precise. Two sweets will go through if the door closes fractionally too late, or the first sweet in the queue will jam in the door if the door closes slightly too soon. Such a simple system is more or less guaranteed to jam before too long.

Some means of properly regulating the flow is required, and Figure 6.15 shows what is probably the simplest mechanism that will do the job. The sweets are piled up in a tube, and there is an opening at the bottom of the tube that is large enough for one sweet to pass through, as in (a). A ramrod or block can pass through an opening on the other side of the tube, and this is moved into the tube to eject the first sweet, as in (b). In (c) the ramrod has been moved back to its original position, the first sweet has been ejected, and the other sweets have all moved down one position.

This method is reasonably jam-proof, and there is little opportunity for extra sweets to escape provided the size of the opening at the bottom of the tube is not too large. It is also very simple, since a reciprocating action is all that is required to eject the sweets. This action can be obtained using either a rack or a cam and piston arrangement. I chose the latter simply because it was something I had not previously tried with the Robotics Invention Kit, and there is probably no major advantage to either method. Two views of the completed robot are shown in Figures 6.16 and 6.17.

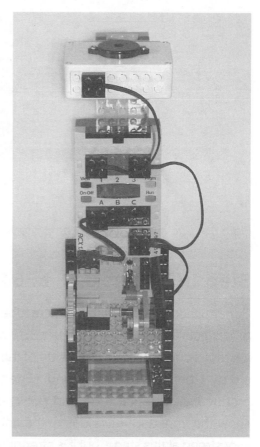

Fig.6.17 Rear view of Sweetiebot

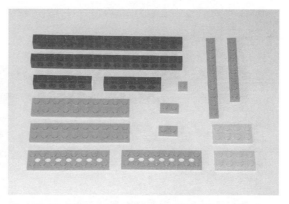

Fig.6.18 The parts needed for the initial stages of construction

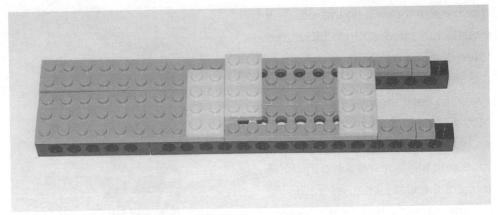

Fig.6.19 The rear side part completed vertical tube

Step 1 (Figures 6.18 to 6.20)

Construction starts with the vertical tube that holds the sweets, and gradually grows outwards from this. Figure 6.18 shows the parts required for the initial stages of construction. Each side of the tube consists of a 16 by 1 beam and a 6 by 1 beam fitted end to end. The two sides are joined by the plates to produce a three unit wide gap between the sides. Figures 6.19 and 6.20 show the front and rear sides of the finished assembly. The structure is not very strong at this stage, but it is strengthened considerably as further sections are added.

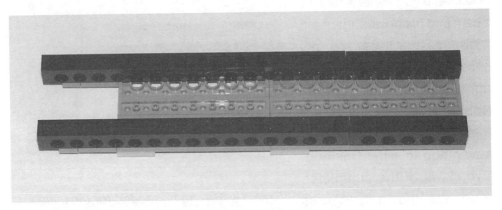

Fig.6.20 The front of the part finished vertical tube

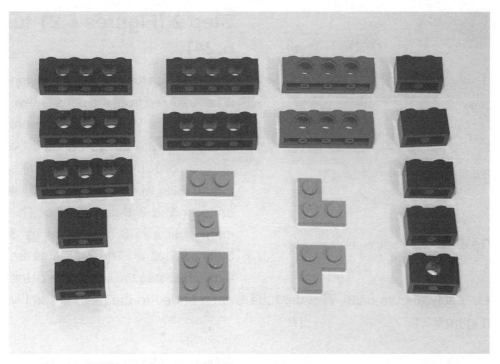

Fig.6.21 *The parts required to build the casing for the block that ejects*
         the sweets

Fig.6.22 *The finished casing,*
         ready for installation

Fig.6.23 *The plates are fitted on*
         the rear of the casing

Fig.6.24 *The casing mounted on the tube*

Step 2 (Figures 6.21 to 6.24)

Next the short tube to hold the piston is constructed from the parts shown in Figure 6.21. With a certain amount of messing around you should be able to produce something like Figure 6.22, which measures 5 by 4 units and is 3 beams high. The internal size is 3 by 2 units by 3 beams in height. The five plates are then fitted onto the underside of the assembly (Figure 6.23), and the tube is then added to the main assembly (Figure 6.24).

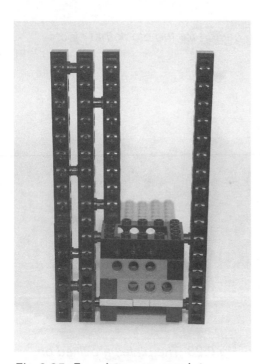

Fig.6.25 *Four beams complete the basic chassis*

Step 3 (Figures 6.25 and 6.26)

Four beams are now added, and these take the motor assembly. Three 16 by 1 beams and a single 10 by 1 beam are used, and they are joined to the chassis and each other using 10 black pegs. Figure 6.25 shows the beams loosely assembled, and this makes it clear how everything fits together. The finished basic chassis is shown in Figure 6.26.

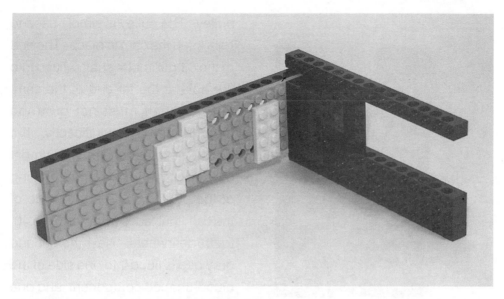

Fig.6.26 The completed basic chassis

Step 4 (Figures 6.27 to 6.30)

The unit is now ready for the piston mechanism to be added. The parts required for the rear section are shown in Figure 6.27, and the rear part of the finished assembly can be seen in Figure 6.28. A 63-millimetre shaft is threaded through the block of three beams, one hole in from the rear of the chassis. A 40-tooth gearwheel is added on the shaft on the outside of the chassis, and a fixing nut is fitted on the shaft on the other side of the beams. A grey peg is fitted into the middle hole of a cam, and the smallest size of pulley is added on the end of the peg. Note that the

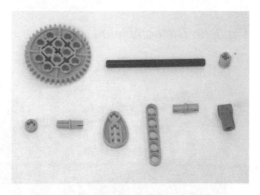

Fig.6.27 The parts for the piston mechanism

peg must be a type that has the standard fitting at one end and a shaft style fitting at the other end, which is the end that connects to the cam and the

Fig.6.28 The finished assembly

Fig.6.29 The completed piston

*Fig.6.30 Another view of the completed
piston mechanism*

pulley. The pulley is simply used to help keep the cam in place. The end of the 63-millimetre shaft is fitted into the hole at the fat end of the cam, but the shaft must not protrude through the cam significantly. If it does, the mechanism will almost certainly jam. The standard fitting of the peg must be on the side of the cam that faces away from the 40-tooth gearwheel. Next the second grey peg is fitted into one side of the blue T-shaped component, and one end of the 5 by 1 half width beam is fitted onto this peg. The other end of this beam is fitted into the peg on the cam.

Next the piston must be made (Figure 6.29), and this just consists of three 2 by 2 bricks fitted one on top of the other. Next a 47-millimetre shaft is fitted into the base of the brick at the bottom of the stack. The piston is then fitted in place and the 43-millimetre shaft is fitted into the base of the blue T-shaped piece. A 4 by 2 plate added to the chassis acts as a guide for the piston shaft. It will probably be necessary to rotate the shaft slightly before it will fit properly.

It may also be necessary to have the 63-millimetre shaft protrude a little further or less far into the chassis in order to get the mechanism working well. There is a 3 by 2 aperture in the chassis, but the piston measures only 2 by 2. This does not prevent it from working properly, and it is not worthwhile redesigning the piston to increase its size to 3 by 2. Doing so will almost certainly result in it jamming.

Fig.6.31 *The mounting pad for the motor*

Step 5 (Figures 6.31 and 6.32)

Next the motor is added. This requires a mounting pad made from two 4 by 2 plates and four 3 by 1 angle plates (Figure 6.31). An eight-toothed gearwheel is fitted onto the shaft of the motor and the motor is then fitted onto the mounting pad (Figure 6.32).

Fig.6.32 *The motor installed on the mounting pad*

Step 6 (Figures 6.33 and 6.34)

The software needs some means of determining when the mechanism has completed one cycle and ejected one sweet, so that the motor can be stopped or a new cycle commenced, as appropriate. On the face of it, the software could simply operate the motor for an apposite amount of time, but with this system things would gradually creep out of synchronisation. The more reliable

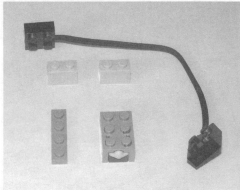

Fig.6.33 The touch sensor and its
associated components

Fig.6.34 The touch sensor in position

Fig.6.35 The beams are built up
using plates

method is to have a sensor that
detects the end of the cycle, or as in
this case, a point very close to the
end of each cycle. A touch sensor
is adequate for this task, and it is
added at the bottom of the tube
section. The parts required are
shown in Figure 6.33, and the end
result is shown in Figure 6.34.

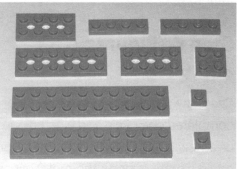

Fig.6.36 The plates for the front
of the tube

Step 7 (Figures 6.35 to 6.37)

To complete the main assembly a number of plates are added to the front of the tube section. First, one or two layers of plates are added on the beams (Figure 6.35). A single layer may be adequate for some types of sweet, but in order to slide down the tube reliably most require a second layer to be added. The sweets are piled up end to end or side to side rather than one on top of the other. Things are done this way simply because as it gives fewer problems with blockages. To prevent the sweets spilling out of the tube the plates shown in Figure 6.36 are added at the front of the tube, giving the finished tube assembly of Figure 6.37.

Fig.6.37 The completed tube

Step 8 (Figures 6.38 to 6.40)

Next the base section is constructed, and the parts required are shown in Figure 6.38. Two of the 12 by 1 beams are joined at both ends using a couple of 8 by 2 plates. An 8 by 1 plate is then placed on top

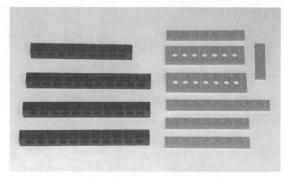

Fig.6.38 The parts for the base section

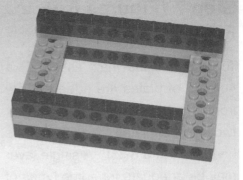

*Fig.6.39 The first stage of building   Fig.6.40 Beams and plates are
          the base completed   used to build up the base*

of each beam (Figure 6.39). The 4 by 1 and 8 by 1 plates are then added along one side on top of the existing plates, and a 12 by 1 beam is then added on top of these. A 10 by 1 plate is then placed on the opposite side of the chassis, and a 10 by 1 beam is added on top of this (Figure 6.40).

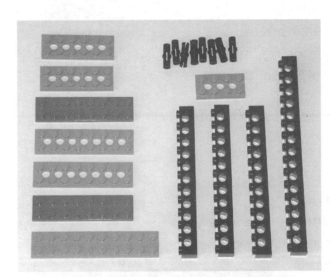

*Fig.6.41 The additional parts needed to
          finish the base*

Step 9 (Figures 6.41 to 6.44)

The parts required to complete the base section are shown in Figure 6.41. Two 8 by 2 plates are added on top of the base section (Figure 6.42), and two further 8 by 2 plates and a 10 by 2 plate are added on the underside. Two 6 by 2 plates and a 4 by 2

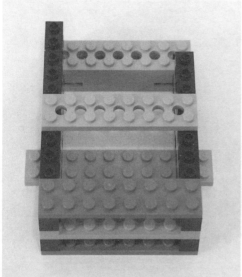

Fig.6.42 The base is strengthened by plates added on top

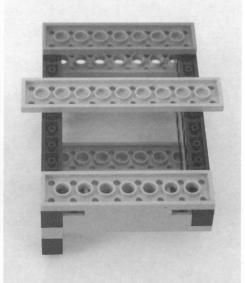

Fig.6.43 Further plates are added on underneath and at one end

plate can be added above one of the 8 by 2 plates to add weight to the base and make it a little more solid (Figure 6.43). In fact this can be done at both ends of the base if you have sufficient plates available. The four vertical beams that carry the main assembly are then added. These are each held in place using two black pegs. Four 12 by 1 beams are required, but you will probably find that there are only three beams of this size left unused. Therefore, three 12 by 1 beams and one 16 by 1 beam are used (Figure 6.44).

Fig.6.44 Four beams carry the main assembly

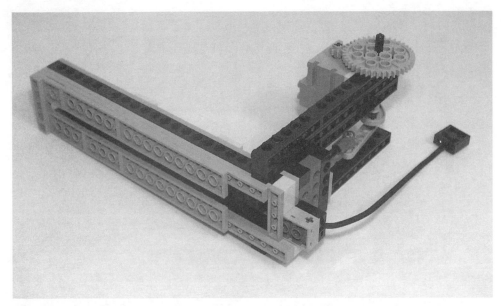

Fig.6.45 The completed main assembly must now be mounted on the base

Fig.6.46 Black pegs are used to mount the main assembly on the base

Step 10 (Figures 6.45 to 6.49)

The main assembly (Figure 6.45) is mounted on the base section, using four black pegs to fix the main assembly onto the four vertical beams of the base section (Figures 6.46 and 6.47). A 10 by 6 plate is added across the vertical beams at the rear of the base section to

Fig.6.47 The mounting viewed from the other side

strengthen and stiffen the unit (Figure 6.48). This gives the virtually complete unit of Figure 6.49, which is ready for the RCX unit and sensor to be added.

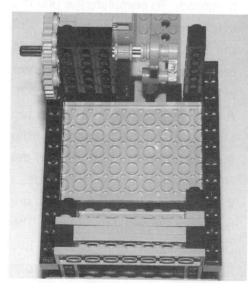

Fig.6.48 A 10 by 6 plate is added across two of the vertical beams to add strength to the unit

Fig.6.49 Nearing completion

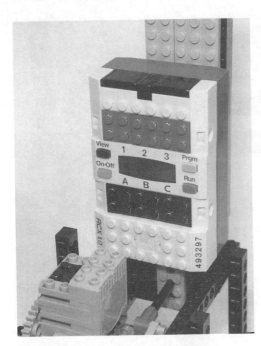

*Fig.6.50 The RCX unit is added
on the rear of the tube*

*Fig.6.51 The sound sensor is added
above the RCX unit*

Step 11 (Figures 6.50 to 6.53)

The RCX unit is mounted vertically on the rear of the tube, as low down as possible (Figure 6.50). It fits onto the three 4 by 2 plates, but this seems to be more than adequate to keep it firmly in place. The sound sensor fits at the top of the tube on its rear side, as far up as possible (Figure 6.51). On the prototype it is mounted via an 8 by 2 plate, but it will fit direct onto the tube if preferred. To complete the unit the sound sensor is wired to input 1 of the RCX unit, the touch switch is connected to input 3, and the motor is wired to output A (Figure 6.52). An ordinary connecting lead is too short to make the connection from the touch sensor to an input of the RCX unit. One of the long leads in the kit could be used, but these are far longer we really need here. The neater solution is to connect two leads together to make a double-length lead. The two connectors that make the join can be anchored on the RCX unit. Sweetiebot is then finished and ready for testing (Figure 6.53).

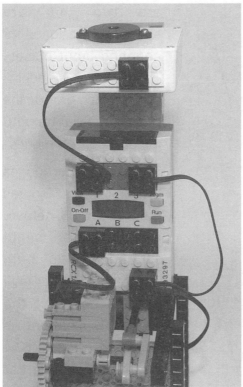

Fig.6.52 *To complete the robot
the leads are fitted*

Fig.6.53 *The completed robot*

Sweetiebot software

In order to understand how the software for Sweetiebot operates it is necessary
to delve into the sensor operating modes that are available. Each hand clap
produces a pulse from the sensor, and we need to count the number of pulses
that occur during a period of time that starts when the first clap is detected.
The period of time needs to be long enough to permit up to about four claps
to be accommodated, but it must not be so long that Sweetiebot appears to
be dim-witted. A period of two seconds seems to be a good compromise. If
you look at the various sensor modes available, you will discover that there

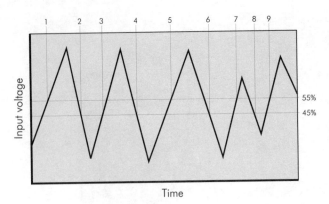

Fig.6.54 *Counting method used in the transition counter mode*

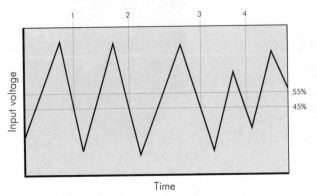

Fig.6.55 *The counting method utilized in the period counter mode*

are two that are specifically designed for counting input pulses. These are input modes 2 and 3, which provide the transient counter and periodic counter modes.

The two counter modes are similar, and Figures 6.54 and 6.55 help to explain the slight difference. In both diagrams the input signal is the same, but the method of counting is different. In Figure 6.54 the transition counter mode is used, and the input value increases by one each time the Boolean input level changes state. In the periodic counter mode (Figure 6.55) the input value is incremented by one each time a complete input pulse has been completed. A hand clap produces one pulse from the sound sensor, or two transitions. The first transition is cause by the increase in sound level at the beginning of the clap, and the decaying sound level produces the second transition as the short burst of sound comes to an end. Either mode could be used in the present application, but the periodic mode provides a count of the hand claps detected, whereas the transition mode would give double the number of claps. The periodic mode is therefore easier to use, and is the one we will utilize in the Sweetiebot software.

Sensor modification

In either of the counter modes the input is used in a form of Boolean operation. In order to drive an RCX input properly the sensor must therefore take the input below 45 percent of the full-scale voltage on negative peaks, and above 55 percent on positive peaks. Using the specified components this might be achieved, but it is quite likely that the minimum output voltage will be too high to produce the required counting action. A slightly quicker response time is also helpful, since it permits hand claps in rapid succession to be counted. Using the original value would tend to merge the pulses into one long pulse, giving a count of one from several claps. However, only a small reduction in the smoothing is acceptable. Reducing the smoothing too much would result in multiple output pulses from each burst of sound. For use with Sweetiebot, or any application that requires Boolean operation, I would recommend the following changes to the components in the sound sensor.

Reduce the value of R6 to 820 ohms

Reduce the value of C4 to 0.47μF (470nF)

Replace D5 and D6 with Schottky diodes (BAR28 or similar)

This is the Visual BASIC listing for Sweetiebot:


```
Private Sub Command1_Click()

With Spirit1

.InitComm

.SelectPrgm 0

.BeginOfTask 0

.SetSensorType 0, 3

.SetSensorMode 0, 3, 0

.Wait 2, 100
```

```
.ClearSensorValue 0

.While 9, 0, 2, 2, 0

.EndWhile

.Wait 2, 200

.SetVar 1, 9, 0

.Loop 0, 1

.On "0"

.While 9, 2, 2, 2, 0

.EndWhile

.While 9, 2, 2, 2, 1

.EndWhile

.Wait 2, 10

.Off "0"

.EndLoop

.StartTask 0

.EndOfTask

End With

End Sub


Private Sub Command2_Click()

Spirit1.CloseComm

End

End Sub
```

The initial part of the program provides the usual initialisation, including the setting of a suitable sensor mode and type. After a one second wait to avoid accidental triggering, the current sensor value is cleared to zero, so that any pulses from sounds during the waiting period are not included in the count. A While...EndWhile loop then provides a hold-off while the value from the sensor remains at zero. The first hand clap increments the input value to one and the program then moves on. A wait instruction delays things for two seconds, which gives the user time to add further hand claps, should he or she wish to do so. The final count is then read from input 1 of the RCX unit and the value is stored in variable 1.

This value is used in a Loop instruction to control the number of loops. The routine in the loop switches on the motor and then uses a While...EndWhile loop to hold things up until the touch sensor is activated. Another While...EndWhile loop then holds things up again until the touch sensor is released again. At this stage the sweet has been dispensed and one cycle has almost been completed. A Wait instruction provides a 0.1 second delay before the motor is switched off, and this ensures that the cycle is properly completed before things are brought to a halt. This routine is repeated until the appropriate number of sweets has been ejected. A StartTask instruction then starts task 0 again, which is a simple way of getting the whole program to loop indefinitely.

Alternative triggering

The sweet dispenser does not have to be sound operated, and a standard Lego light or touch sensor could be used to trigger it instead. I suppose the obvious alternative to the sound sensor is a touch type operated by way of coins. The simple mechanism shown partly finished in Figure 6.56 and completed in Figure 6.57 will operate with two-pence coins. It is based on a 10 by 2 plate, which has a 4 x 2 plate fitted on top and right at one end. The touch sensor is added on top of this and then a connector is fitted to the sensor. A 4 by 2 angle plate is fitted on the base plate, and it is positioned so that it almost touches the front of the sensor. The sensor is activated when the coin goes through the narrow gap between the sensor and the angle plate. A 2 by 2 plate is fitted next to the angle plate, and the first stage of construction is then complete.

Fig.6.56 The initial stage of building the coin mechanism

The assembly must now be built up to provide a slot of appropriate size for the coin. A 4 by 2 brick is placed on top of the angle plate and the 2 by 2 plate, and then two 2 by 2 bricks are added on top of this. A pair of 4 by 2 plates is then added on top of these. Next a 2 by 2 brick is added on top of the connector on the touch switch. Finally, a 6 by 2 plate is added at the top of the assembly to provide a "roof" to the slot.

Results are likely to be best if the coin mechanism is mounted horizontally so that gravity helps the coin on its way through the slot. Touch sensors can sometimes be a bit reluctant to operate. If coins passing through the slot fail

Fig.6.57 The finished coin mechanism ready for installation

to operate the sensor reliably, or at all, a piece of paper or thin card glued to the angle plate will narrow the slot and should get things working properly. Fix the card or paper in place with something like Bostik Blu-Tack, so that it can be easily removed again without damaging the angle plate. This mechanism can be used as a simple trigger to get the robot started, but it also seems to work quite well if used with an input set to the counting mode. Remember that the touch switch, unlike the sound sensor, is a passive device, and it should not be used with an input that is for operation with an active sensor.

Pot-pourri

Bouncing back

The Lego touch sensors can be used to detect when a robot has collided with something so that corrective measures can be taken. This is a rather clumsy way of doing things though, and it is clearly better to have a type of sensor that will detect obstacles before the robot actually hits them. With some form of "eye", the robot can steer around any obstacles and avoid continually blundering into things. The Lego light sensor can be used to detect objects, and it can be made more effective with the aid of the infrared transmitter in the RCX unit. This process is covered in BP901, Introducing Robotics with Lego MindStorms, and will not be described again here.

Using light sensors is quite effective, but it also has a definite limitation. The robot knows there is an object to avoid when the light reflected from an object is detected, but it does not know the distance to the object. If the obstacle happens to be particularly reflective it is likely that the robot will take steps to avoid it long before there is any need to do so. A better way of doing things is to use the radar approach, where it is not just a reflected signal that is of importance, but the time taken for the signal to be reflected back to the source. The speed of the signal is known, and the distance of any detected object can therefore be calculated for the delay between transmission and reception. Using light in this way is extremely difficult at short distances due to very short delay between transmission and reception. Light travels at 300 million metres per second, so the time taken to do a round trip of under a metre is clearly going to be very short indeed! In fact it would take just a few nanoseconds.

Things are much easier if sound is used, due to the much lower speed of sound waves. Sound takes roughly three milliseconds to travel a metre, giving a delay of around six milliseconds when an object is detected one metre from the transmitter. A delay of this order is still quite short, but is very easily detected and measured using electronic circuits. Ultrasonics is normally used with this method of measuring. In other words, the sound waves are at frequencies above the upper limit of human hearing. This means using frequencies of 20 kilohertz or more and in practice most systems operate at 40 kilohertz. Of course, bats use this method of echo location to "see" in the dark, and the bat version apparently operates at frequencies from about 25 kilohertz to around 100 kilohertz. The exact frequency varies somewhat from one bat to another of the same species, and considerably from one species to another.

The short wavelengths of ultrasonic sound enable an echo location system to detect relatively small objects. Even so, do not expect a system of this type to locate very small objects, particularly at longer ranges. Another advantage of ultrasonics is that sound waves at these high frequencies are highly directional. This helps to minimise problems with direct pick-up from the transmitter and keeps things very simple. A further advantage of using ultrasonics is that you do not hear a stream of annoying "beeps" while the system is in operation. However keen your hearing happens to be, you will hear no sound at all from the system. Note though, that some pets might be able to hear the signal, and might vacate the area when the system is used.

System operation

The block diagram of Figure 7.1 helps to explain the way in which this sensor circuit operates. A 40-kilohertz oscillator generates a signal that is fed to a special transducer that converts the electrical signal into corresponding sound waves. This oscillator is gated (switched on and off) by a second oscillator that operates at a much lower frequency, and produces short pulses. Consequently, the 40-kilohertz oscillator produces short signal bursts several times per second. The low frequency oscillator is also used to set a flip-flop, which is a very basic logic circuit. The pulse from the low frequency oscillator sends the output of the flip-flop to logic 1, which in this case means to about 6 volts or so. A pulse to the reset input sends the output to logic 0 again, or to little more than zero volts in other words. An amplifier

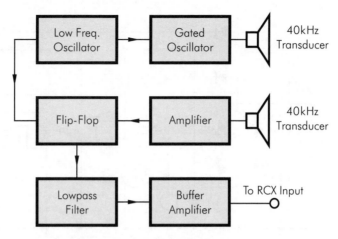

Fig.7.1 The block diagram for the ultrasonic ranging system

that is fed from a special transducer provides the reset pulse. The transducer operates as a microphone that is very inefficient with normal sounds, but is very efficient at frequencies around 40 kilohertz. The reflected 40-kilohertz transmissions are therefore picked up by this transducer, amplified, and then used to reset the flip-flop.

The output signal from the flip-flop is therefore a series of pulses, and the duration of each pulse depends on the time taken for the reflected sound to reach the receiving transducer. The greater the distance from the sensor to the detected object, the longer the duration of the pulses. This provides a pulse length that is roughly proportional to the distance to detected objects, but what we require is a voltage that can be read by the RCX unit. In order to obtain a suitable voltage it is merely necessary to feed the pulses through a lowpass filter. This smoothes the signal to produce an output voltage that is equal to the average voltage of the pulse signal.

At short distances the pulses are short and there are long gaps between them, giving a low average voltage. At long ranges the pulses are much longer and the gap between them is much shorter, giving a high average output potential. The circuit therefore provides the required distance-to-voltage conversion. The output voltage of the lowpass filter drives the input of the RCX unit via the usual buffer amplifier stage, etc.

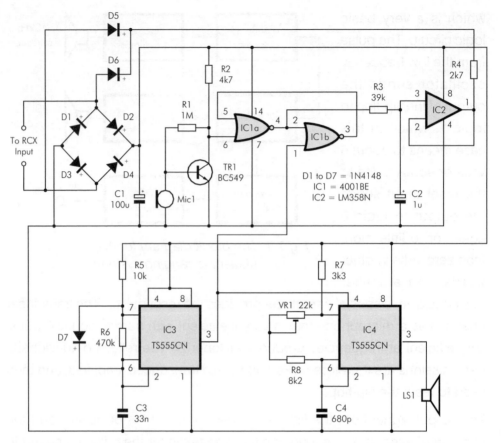

Fig.7.2 The circuit diagram for the ultrasonic sensor

Circuit operation

Refer to Figure 7.2 for the full circuit diagram of the ultrasonic sensor. The upper left-hand section of the circuit is the usual power supply and diode mixer circuit. TR1 is the amplifier in the receiver part of the circuit, and this is a high-gain common emitter amplifier. A unit of this type would normally require high sensitivity so that the longest possible operating range was obtained. In this case we are really only interested in detecting objects up to a metre or so from the sensor, and the relatively small amount of gain provided by a single transistor is just about adequate. Mic1 is the receiving transducer, and it is a piezo-electric device. It operates much like a crystal microphone, but it only works efficiently at 40 kilohertz. There is a potential problem with noise and vibration picked up by the microphone causing the flip-flop to be reset prematurely. However, the efficiency of Mic1 is so low at audio frequencies that this does not seem to be a problem in practice.

The flip-flop is based on two of the CMOS 2-input NOR gates in IC1, and it uses a conventional arrangement for a basic set/reset flip-flop. The other two gates in IC1 are not used, but their inputs are tied to one or other of the supply rails on the circuit board. This prevents spurious operation and possible static damage to these inputs, but is otherwise of no consequence. One input of the flip-flop is driven directly from the collector of TR1, and the bias level of TR1 is such that its collector is normally at what counts as a logic 0 potential for a CMOS logic device. The collector of TR1 goes to a logic 1 potential on the first positive output half-cycle when a signal is picked up by the microphone, resetting the flip-flop in the process.

Resistor R3 and capacitor C2 form a simple lowpass filter. This circuit needs to have a long enough time constant to give a reasonably smooth DC output signal. On the other hand, the time constant must also be short enough to give the circuit a suitably fast response time, since the robot might otherwise crash into things before the reading changed to indicate that an obstacle had been detected. IC2 is the buffer amplifier at the output of the circuit. This is one section of an LM358N dual operational amplifier, and no connections are made to the other section of the device.

The lower section of the circuit is the transmitter, and it is based on two 555 timer devices (IC3 and IC4) used in minor variations of the standard oscillator mode. IC3 is used in the low frequency oscillator. We require a circuit that provides brief positive output pulses, but the standard oscillator configuration provides an output waveform where the high output period is longer than the low duration. Steering diode D7 is therefore used to change the normal charge and discharge action of C3. The output at pin 3 of IC3 goes high while C3 is charging. It charges through the relatively low resistance of R5 and D7, giving the required short positive periods. The output of IC3 is low while C3 discharges, and the discharge path is through the high resistance of R6 and

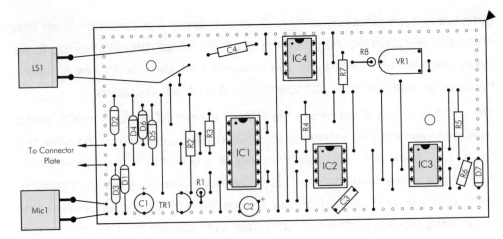

Fig.7.3 The component layout and wiring

the low resistance of an internal switching transistor of IC3. The high value of R6 provides the long periods between the positive output pulses.

IC3's output is used to provide the set pulses to one input of the flip-flop, and to control the gate input of the 40-kilohertz oscillator. The latter is based on IC4, and it is controlled via the reset input at pin 4. IC4 oscillates normally while pin 4 is high, but is disabled when this pin is taken low. The high output pulses from IC3 therefore provide the short bursts of signal from IC4. VR1 enables the operating frequency of IC4 to be adjusted to the optimum frequency for the two transducers. LS1 is the transmitting transducer, and this is a piezo-electric device, much like the receiving transducer.

Construction

The stripboard layout and wiring for the ultrasonic sensor are shown in Figure 7.3. The underside view of the board showing the breaks in the copper strips appears in Figure 7.4. The board measures 40 holes by 19 copper strips, but I had to trim away two corners slightly in order to get the board to fit into the case utilized for the prototype sensor. This may or may not be necessary, depending on the case you use. I used a white plastic box having approximate outside dimensions of 111 by 57 by 22 millimetres. Construction of the board largely follows along conventional lines.

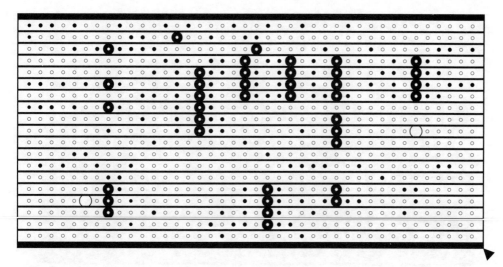

Fig.7.4 The underside of the ultasonic sensor board

The 4001BE used for IC1 is a CMOS device, and it is therefore vulnerable to damage from static charges. It should be supplied in some form of anti-static packing, such as conductive foam or a plastic tube. Leave this component in the protective packing until it is time for it to be fitted to the board, which is not until the unit is otherwise finished. It must be fitted to the board via a socket, so that soldered connections to the integrated circuit itself are avoided. The pins should be handled as little as possible while it is being fitted into place, but they will probably have to be squeezed inwards slightly in order to get the device to fit into the socket.

The other three integrated circuits are not vulnerable to small static charges, but it is still a good idea to fit them on the board via holders. IC3 and IC4 can be any low power version of the 555 timer. The standard 555 timer is not suitable since the increased current consumption could load the supply voltage to the point where the circuit fails to work properly. Ideally TR1 should be a BC549C, which is the highest gain version of the BC549. Correct operation should be obtained using other BC549s, but it is possible that the value of R1 will have to be reduced slightly in order to obtain a suitably low quiescent voltage at the collector of TR1. It is not essential to use a BC549, and any

Fig.7.5 The completed ultrasonic ranging board

high gain silicon NPN transistor should work well in this circuit. However, bear in mind that alternatives could have a different case style and (or) leadout configuration. If you use an alternative device make sure that it is connected correctly.

The top and underside of the finished board are shown in Figures 7.5 and 7.6 respectively. The finished circuit board is mounted inside the case using metric M2.5 or 6BA fixings, including extra nuts to act as spacers between the case and the board.

The ultrasonic transducers are normally purchased as a matched pair. They may be identical, and it clearly makes no difference which one is used for LS1 and which one is used as Mic1 if this is the case. These days it is more common for the two transducers to be different, and it is then essential to get them the right way around if optimum performance is to be achieved. The retailer's literature should make it clear which unit is which. Usually the receiving transducer (Mic1) is marked with a type number that starts with a letter "R", while the transmitting transducer (LS1) has a type number that begins with a "T".

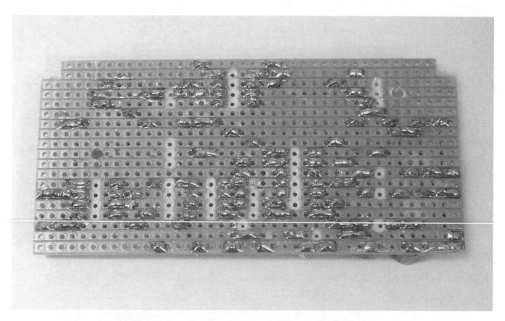

Fig.7.6 The underside of the ultrasonic ranging board

It is unlikely that the ultrasonic transducers will have any mounting flanges or anything of this nature. The normal way of mounting them on a case is to drill small holes to accommodate the pins at the rear of each component, and then glue them to the front panel using a good gap-filling adhesive. An epoxy adhesive is suitable, or a glue gun will do the job almost instantly. Be careful not to get any adhesive onto the pins, as this could make it difficult to make the soldered connections to them. The pins may protrude too far into the case so that they are obstructed by the circuit board. If so, they must be trimmed slightly using ordinary wire cutters prior to mounting them on the case. If the receiving transducer has one pin connected to the case, this pin should be the one that connects to the 0-volt supply rail of the circuit (the lower pin in Figure 7.3).

A hole to take the lead that goes to the connector plate is drilled in the lid of the case. A two-way lead about 100 millimetres long is threaded through the lid and then connected to the connector plate. The plate is then fixed to the lid using a good gap-filling adhesive, and the lead is connected to the apposite

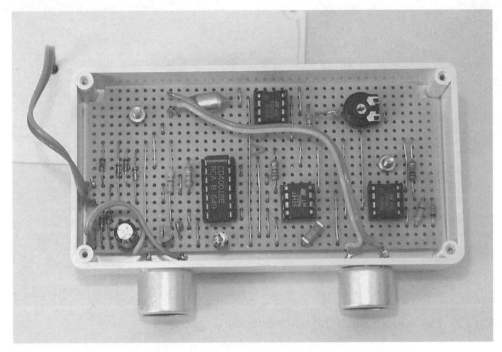

Fig.7.7 Interior view of the completed ultrasonic ranging sensor

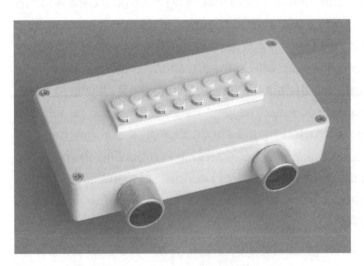

Fig.7.8 The finished sensor, complete with a connector plate mounted on the top

pair of pins on the circuit board. A 6 by 2 or 8 by 2 Lego brick is glued to the underside of the case so that the sensor can be easily mounted on your robots. An interior view of the completed sensor is shown in Figure 7.7, and an exterior view appears in Figure 7.8.

Components list

Resistors, all 0.25 watt 5% carbon film

R1   1M (brown, black, green, gold)

R2   4k7 (yellow, violet, red, gold)

R3   39k (orange, white, orange, gold)

R4   2k7 (red, violet, red, gold)

R5   10k (brown, black, orange, gold)

R6   470k (yellow, violet, yellow, gold)

R7   3k3 (orange, orange, red, gold)

R8   8k2 (grey, red, red, gold)

Potentiometer

VR1   22k miniature horizontal preset

Capacitors

C1 100μ 10V PC electrolytic

C2 1μ 50V PC electrolytic

C3   33n polyester

C4   680p polystyrene

Semiconductors

IC1   4001BE

IC2   LM358C or LM358N

IC3,4   TS555CN (2 off)

D1 to D7   1N4148 (7 off)

TR1   BC549 or similar

Miscellaneous

LS1/Mic1   Matched pair of 40kHz ultrasonic transducers

Plastic case about 111 by 57 by 22 millimetres

0.1-inch pitch stripboard having 40 holes by 19 copper strips

14-pin DIL holder for IC1

8-pin DIL holders for IC2 to IC4 (3 off)

8 by 2 connector plate

6BA or M2.5 fixings

6 by 2 or 8 by 2 Lego brick

Wire, solder-pins, solder, etc.

Testing

The MindStorms software obviously has no specific provision for an ultrasonic ranging device, but the sensor "looks" the same as a light sensor as far as the RCX unit is concerned. The ultrasonic sensor can therefore be tested using the View facility and an input set up for standard operation with a light sensor. VR1 should initially be set at a roughly central setting. If you have access to suitable test equipment, the easiest way to give VR1 the optimum setting is to first remove IC3 from its holder. Make sure the power is switched off when you do this and that IC3 is carefully prised free using a small screwdriver so that its pins are not buckled. IC4 should oscillate continuously when the unit is switched back on again. With the transducers aimed at a wall about half a metre away, monitor the signal level at the collector of TR1 and adjust VR1 for maximum reading. Switch off again, replace IC3, and the unit is then ready for use.

In the absence of suitable test equipment locating the optimum setting for VR1 becomes a matter of trial and error. With the sensor aimed at a wall about 300 to 500 millimetres away, there should be no difficulty in finding a setting that gets the unit to work. As the sensor is moved closer to the wall the reading will increase, while moving it away from the wall will have the opposite effect. If the sensor is moved too far away the reading will suddenly fall to zero, and the unit is then out of range. With further adjustment of VR1 it will probably be possible to obtain an in-range reading again.

With a little experimentation it should be possible to get the sensor operating with a maximum range of at least one metre. With careful adjustment it may well operate properly at somewhat longer ranges, but the absolute maximum is under two metres, and typically the unit will operate at ranges of up to about 1.5 metres or so. The minimum reading achievable in raw mode will be at something more than point-blank range and saturation occurs at approximately 150 millimetres.

Batbot software

If the light sensors are omitted, the ultrasonic sensor fits easily onto 20/20bot, which then becomes Batbot. The easiest place to add the sensor is on top of the RCX unit (Figure 7.9). Some very simple software is all that is needed to

get Batbot exploring, and the RCX code of Figure 7.10 will do the job. The first "brick" switches on the two motors and then the program goes into an infinite loop. This sets both motors to go forward and then a Wait Until block provides a hold-off until the value returned from the sensor is 50 or more. Obviously RCX code does not specifically

Fig.7.9 The sensor fitted to a rover type robot

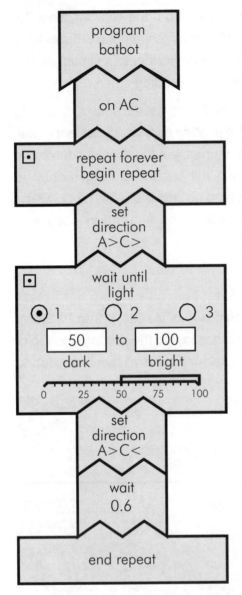

Fig.7.10 The RCX code for Batbot

cater for an ultrasonic sensor, but selecting a light sensor provides the right input characteristics for the ultrasonic sensor. I used a threshold value of 50, but any valid value can be used here. The RCX unit's View facility can be used to find the reading produced with the Batbot at the required operating range.

The program moves on once the Wait Until block has detected a suitable reading and motor C is then set into reverse so that Batbot starts to turn. A wait instruction keeps the robot turning for 0.6 seconds, and then the program moves back to the beginning of the loop where the motors are set to go forward again.

VB version

This Visual BASIC program closely follows the scheme of things used in the RCX code version of the Batbot software:

```
Private Sub Command1_Click()
With Spirit1
.InitComm
.SelectPrgm 1
.BeginOfTask 0
.SetSensorType 0, 3
.On "02"
```

```
.Loop 2, 0
.SetFwd "02"
.While 9, 0, 1, 2, 50
.EndWhile
.SetRwd "2"
.Wait 2, 60
.EndLoop
.EndOfTask
End With
End Sub


Private Sub Command2_Click()
Spirit1.CloseComm
End
End Sub
```

This follows the original method so closely that it does not really warrant any
further comment. One slight problem with both the RCX and Visual BASIC
versions of the Batbot software is that the robot always turns in the same
direction when an obstruction is detected. This version of the Visual BASIC
software has been modified to make the robot turn left or right, purely at
random:

```
Private Sub Command1_Click()
With Spirit1
.InitComm
.SelectPrgm 1
.BeginOfTask 0
```

```
.SetSensorType 0, 3
.On "02"
.Loop 2, 0
.SetFwd "02"
.While 9, 0, 1, 2, 50
.EndWhile
.SetVar 1, 4, 100
.If 0, 1, 0, 2, 50
.SetRwd "2"
.Else
.SetRwd "0"
.EndIf
.Wait 2, 60
.EndLoop
.EndOfTask
End With
End Sub
Private Sub Command2_Click()
Spirit1.CloseComm
End
End Sub
```

The random element is produced by first placing a random number in variable
1. This is achieved by using a SetVar command with a source number of 4
(the random number generator) and a value parameter of 100. This limits the
number generated to a maximum value of 100. An If...Then...Else structure
then reverses motor A if the value in variable 1 is greater than 50, or reverses
motor C if it is not, giving the required randomisation of the turning direction.

If preferred, Batbot can be given a deliberate bias one way or the other by altering the value of 50 used in the If instruction. The amount of turn could also be randomised by generating another random number and using it in the Wait instruction.

Hootbot

Even if your interest in robotics is quite new, you will no doubt have noticed the recent popularity of various types of so-called virtual pets. Strictly speaking a virtual pet is one produced by software running on a computer, and presented to the user via a screen, virtual-reality headset, or whatever. If the "animal" has motors, gears, and a built-in processor it is not really a virtual pet, but is more what might be termed a robopet. Anyway, these robot pets are now widely called virtual pets, and that is the term we will use here. The Robotics Invention System is probably not suitable for producing something comparable to the sophisticated virtual puppy made by a well-known Japanese electronics company, but it has everything needed to produce some amusing virtual pets.

Fig.7.11 Front view of Hootbot

Hootbot (Figures 7.11 and 7.12) is designed to entertain small children, but seems to get a laugh from most children in the 0 to 100+ age group! Hootbot is a virtual owl that stands on its perch until it gets dark enough for him (or her) to wake up. Most owls are nocturnal of course, and sleep in the daytime.

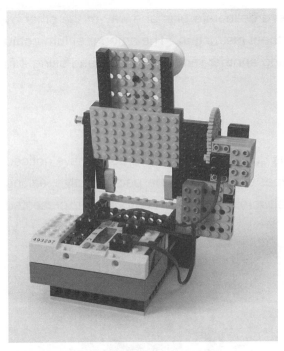

Fig.7.12 The rear of Hootbot

When it gets dark enough, Hootbot wakes up, gets excited, and does three backward somersaults while doing an owl-like tawit-tawoo sound. Well, it does a sort of vaguely owl-like sound effect anyway. After a brief pause, in another fit of exuberance Hootbot does three somersaults in the opposite direction while repeating the sound effect.

Rotation sensor

This robot demonstrates the use of the Lego rotation sensor, which is a very useful and perhaps underrated part of the Lego MindStorms system. Note that this sensor is not included in the Robotics Invention System, and that it must purchased from one of the companies that sell Lego spares and accessories. Fortunately, it is not one of the more expensive sensors.

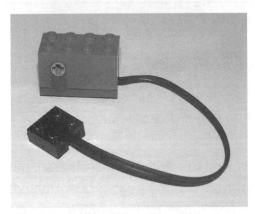

Fig.7.13 The Lego rotation sensor

This device looks a bit like a taller version of the Lego light sensor (Figure 7.13), but instead of the opto-devices at the front it has a hole for a shaft that goes in one side and out the other.

The RCX unit has a specific mode for use with the rotation sensor, and this gives a count of the rotations. To be more precise, it counts each increment of 22.5 degrees, which means that the count actually goes up by 16 per complete 360-degree rotation. Rotation in one direction increments the count, while rotation in the opposite direction decrements it. The maximum values that can be handled using Spirit.OCX are plus and minus 32766. Using RCX code it appears as though the limits are plus and minus 500 if you look at the analogue scale. However, if you enter larger values into the text boxes the analogue scale will change accordingly. The limits do actually remain at plus and minus 32766 when using RCX code.

Increased resolution

At 22.5 degrees the resolution of the sensor is inadequate for many applications, but the effective resolution can be set much higher if necessary. The increased resolution is obtained by having a step-up ratio from the monitored shaft to the one that drives the rotation sensor. Suppose that the monitored shaft is fitted with a 24-tooth gearwheel that drives an 8-tooth type on the shaft in the rotation sensor. This gives a 1 to 3 step-up ratio, and the rotation sensor therefore goes through three degrees of rotation for every one-degree of change on the monitored shaft. This gives a threefold improvement in resolution, taking it from 22.5 degrees to 7.5 degrees. The higher the step-up ratio used the higher the resolution that is obtained.

The rotation sensor is apparently an optical device, which detects four different shades of grey marked on a small drum that is rotated by the shaft fitted in the sensor. This gives four different analogue readings as the shaft is rotated, and the changes in readings enable the software to determine the direction of the rotation as well as the amount of rotation. The firmware in the RCX unit handles all this provided the correct sensor mode (angle mode) is selected.

Note that the firmware for the rotation and temperature sensors is not enabled by default. In order to use angle mode or either type of temperature mode you must run the Robotics Invention System software, then select Enter, Getting Started, and Set Up Options. Switch on the RCX unit and bring it within range of the infrared tower. This should clear the error message from the screen. Next select Advanced from the bottom of the screen, and then click on the cross by the Rotation sensors entry to change it to a tick. If you wish to enable the temperature sensor firmware as well, also click on the cross beside the Temperature sensors entry. Click on the Go Back button to return to the previous screen, and then operate the Main Menu button. When asked if you wish to save your changes select Yes.

The RCX unit is then ready for use with the new type or types of sensor that you selected. If the firmware is reinstalled at some later time, it will be necessary to repeat this process in order to resume operation with temperature or rotation sensors.

Fig.7.14 The part completed base

Step 1 (Figures 7.14 and 7.15)

Construction starts with the base, which consists of two 16 by 1 beams joined by a 10 x 1 beam and an 8 x 1 beam at each end. Two 10 by 2 plates at each end hold everything together. A 10 by 1 plate is added between the 16 by 1 beams, and this forms part of the mounting for the RCX unit. Figure 7.14 shows the underside of the base before two of the plates have been added, and this shows how everything fits together. The completed base section appears in Figure 7.15.

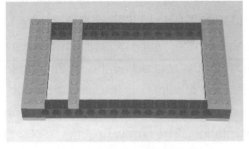

Fig.7.15 The completed base section

Step 2 (Figures 7.16 and 7.17)

The base is now built up using further beams and plates. The raised side pieces provide a mounting for the two side sections. First two 8 by 1 beams are added on the sides, and then two 6 by 1 plates are added onto these.

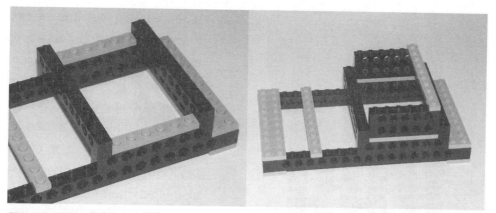

Fig.7.16 Building up the base   Fig.7.17 The completed base

Then two 10 by 1 cross beams are added (Figure 7.16). Two 6 by 1 beams are then stacked on each of the 6 by 1 plates. Finally, a 10 by 1 plate is fitted across these two main beams (Figure 7.17).

Step 3 (Figures 7.18 to 7.21)

Now construction moves to the vertical platform that carries the drive mechanism and the rotation sensor. It is based on eight beams giving the shape shown in Figure 7.18. Two each of these sizes are required:

2 by 1

8 by 1

12 by 1

16 by 1

They are held together using pegs, which are visible in the loosened assembly shown in Figure 7.19. Ideally the pegs should all be of the

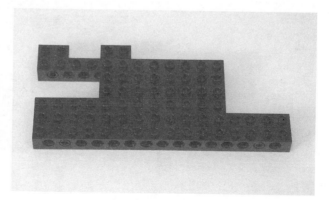

Fig.7.18 The basic platform

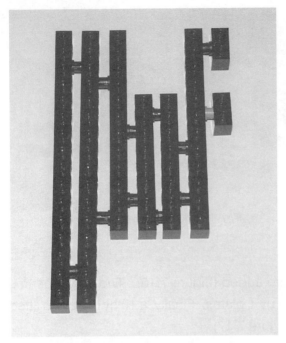

black variety, but one or two grey ones can be used to ensure that there are sufficient black pegs left for subsequent stages of construction. Next a number of plates are added on the front and rear faces of the platform. Two black pegs are also fitted into one of the 16 by 1 beams, and these will eventually be used to fix the platform to the base section. The plates and pegs are all shown in Figures 7.20 and 7.21.

Fig.7.19 The platform is held together by pegs

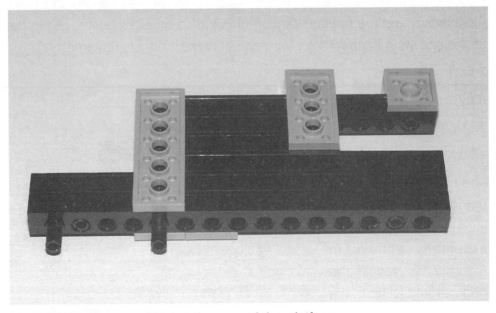

Fig.7.20 Plates are added at the rear of the platform

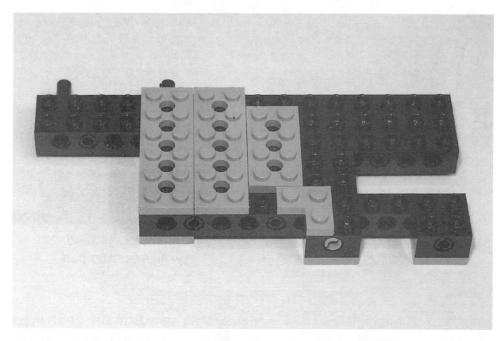

Fig.7.21 Further plates are added on the other side of the platform

Step 4 (Figure 7.22 to 7.25)

To complete the vertical platform assembly the rotation sensor and the motor are added. Before installing the rotation sensor it should be fitted with a 21-millimetre shaft, and the shaft should then be fitted with an 8-tooth gearwheel at one end and the smallest size of pulley at the other (Figure 7.22). The pulley simply acts as a retaining

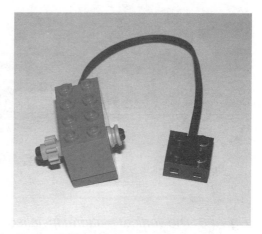

Fig.7.22 The rotation sensor fitted with the drive shaft

"nut" incidentally, and the drive to the sensor is via the gearwheel. The rotation sensor is then fitted on the platform in the position shown in Figure 7.23. Fit

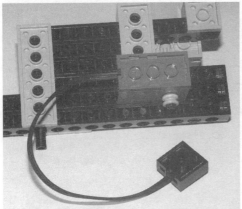

Fig.7.23 *The rotation sensor in position on the platform*

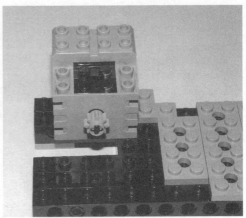

Fig.7.24 *The motor installed on its mounting pad*

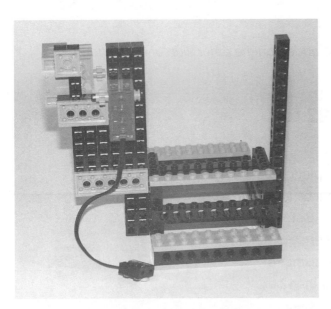

Fig.7.25 *The vertical platform installed on the base. A 16 by 1 beam is fitted opposite this on the other side of the base*

an 8-tooth gearwheel onto the shaft of the motor and then fit it onto the platform (Figure 7.24). Substantially less than the full base area of the motor is supported by the platform, but the motor should still be well and truly fixed in position. The completed platform is mounted on the base section using two black pegs, and a 16 by 1 beam is fitted on the other side of the base using the same method of fixing (Figure 7.25).

Step 5 (Figures 7.26 to 7.28)

Next the owl is created. You may prefer to "do your own thing here", but if so, remember that the owl must be no more than 10 units wide if it is to fit onto the base section. Also, it must go no more than about eight units above or below the pivot point. If you copy my creation, start by building the sides from four 10 by 1 beams and four black pegs. Figure 7.26 shows an assembled side section and one that is ready for the two beams to be fitted together. Incidentally, the side pieces are "mirror images" of each other. The two sides are joined together using a number of plates, as shown in Figure 7.27. The parts required are two 10 by 1 plates, two 10 x 2 plates, and three 8 x 2 types. A couple of 2 by 1 plates are also fitted to the side pieces. Two 2 by 1 bricks are fitted onto the plates (Figure 7.28), but note that these are the green bricks that have an X-shaped hole to take a drive shaft. The ordinary type that has a round hole is unsuitable. The drive to the owl is carried through one of these bricks, and the drive shaft must not be free to rotate inside the brick.

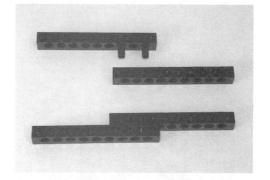

Fig.7.26 Construction of the owl starts with the sides

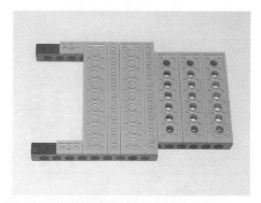

Fig.7.27 The sides are held together using various plates

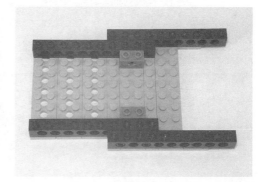

Fig.7.28 A special 2 by 1 brick carries the drive to the owl

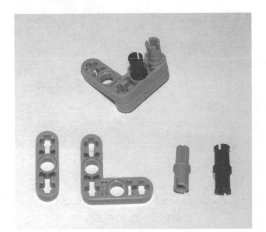

Fig.7.29 *The parts for one foot and a completed foot*

Step 6 (Figures 7.29 and 7.30)

Next the feet are added to the legs. Figure 7.29 shows the parts required for one foot, together with a completed foot. The completed feet, which are "mirror images", are fitted to the legs using two pegs per foot. To complete the owl a face and some additional plates can be added (Figure 7.30). The eyes use the same black and white pieces that were used as the basis of the eyes for Camerashybot. The beak consists of a yellow 2 by 1 brick and a sloping yellow 2 by 1 brick. A black peg is used to fit the beak onto the main assembly. Various plates are then fitted to give a little more colour to the owl, and to add spots, stripes, or whatever texture takes your fancy.

Fig.7.30 *The completed owl*

Step 7 (Figures 7.31 and 7.32)

To fix the owl onto the main unit start by fitting a 63-millimetre shaft into the left-hand side (left-wing side?) of the owl, so that it goes through the green brick and almost touches the second green brick. Place the protruding end of the shaft into the top hole in the side section that carries the motor, and then push it outwards into the side section. Hold a 40-tooth gearwheel on the outside of the side section and push the shaft right through the side piece and into the gearwheel. This gearwheel should mesh nicely with the 8-tooth type on the motor's shaft. Next push a 39-millimetre shaft into the top hole of the other side section, and through the side of the owl until it emerges from the green brick. Place a fixing "nut" on the end of the shaft to help keep it in place. This

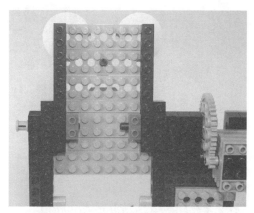

Fig.7.31 *The owl fitted onto the main unit*

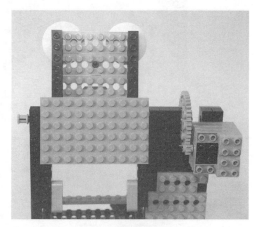

Fig.7.32 *A large plate acts as the back of the owl*

gives the completed mounting of Figure 7.31. Finally, add a 10 by 6 plate to act as the back of the owl (Figure 7.32).

Step 8 (Figures 7.33 to 7.35)

The RCX unit is now fitted on the base section, and the underside view of Figure 7.33 shows how it fits into place. To complete Hootbot the light sensor is fitted on the vertical platform, and the motor, light sensor and rotation sensor

Fig.7.33 The RCX unit in position

Fig.7.34 The connections to the RCX unit

are respectively connected to output A, input 3, and input 1 of the RCX unit (Figure 7.34). The completed robot (Figure 7.35) is then ready for testing.

Alternative gearing

The 5 to 1 reduction gearing from the motor to the drive shaft gives a relatively slow maximum somersault rate from the owl. Using a 16-tooth gearwheel on the motor gives a higher maximum speed and a more amusing effect, but it also increases the risk of the owl "coming apart at the seams" as it goes through its routine. Anyway, if you would prefer a more athletic owl the mounting pad for the motor should be built up so that it is one plate thicker than previously.

This provides the greater space required to accommodate a 16-tooth gearwheel (Figure 7.36).

Owl command

The RCX code for Hootbot utilizes a user-defined command, and the code for this is shown in Figure 7.37. All this does is to generate a simple owl-like sound effect that is used twice in the main RCX program. You can either define the owl command and then use it in the main program, or you can simply insert the series of seven Tone commands in the main program in place of the owl command. This second method is less neat, and it will also make the main program very long. In fact it could well require a metre or more of virtual screen.

Figure 7.37 shows the Hootbot RCX code. Even with the aid of a user-defined command, the program is quite long, and it has therefore been broken into two sections

Fig.7.35 The completed Hootbot robot

in Figure 7.38. It is, of course, entered onto the screen in one long series of commands. The first program block simply sets a power level for the motor. I would suggest a medium power initially, but you can obviously use any power level that gets the owl to perform satisfactorily. Next the program must wait for the light sensor to detect a suitably low level of illumination, and this is

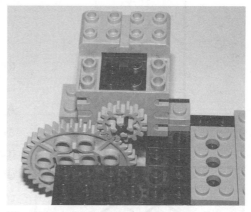

Fig.7.36 The motor fitted with a 16-tooth gearwheel

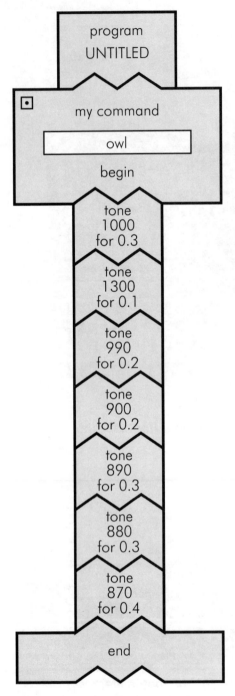

Fig.7.37 The owl user routine

achieved using a wait until block having a threshold level of 42. Of course, you must use a threshold level that gives good results with the particular sensor you are using, and the prevailing light level. Remember that the View facility can be used to check the readings from the light sensor.

The program moves on once a suitably low light level has been detected, and the owl command is produced first. This takes 1.8 seconds, but the program moves on to the next program block almost at once. The owl sound effect is therefore produced while the owl goes through its somersaults. The next instruction sets the motor into reverse, but this actually produces forwards somersaults from the owl. We require the motor to be switched on while the owl goes through three somersaults, which produces a total count of 240. Bear in mind that the step-up gearing to the rotation sensor means that the count is 80 per complete rotation, and not 16. A repeat while block keeps the motor switched on while the count is no more than 240, but the program moves on once the count exceeds this figure. An off instruction then switches off the motor, and a delay of one second is provided by a wait instruction.

Another owl command is then performed so that the sound effect is generated a second time, and a direction command sets the motor to go forwards. This produces backward somersaults. Another repeat until block then switches on the motor and keeps it switched on while the count is between 2 and 255. The higher figure of 255 may seem to be excessive, since the count should not exceed 241. In practice it is likely that a certain amount of overshoot will occur, and the higher figure used in this command must take this factor into account. The figure of 255 is

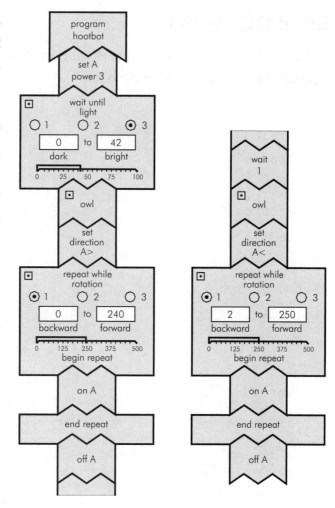

Fig.7.38 The main Hootbot program

comfortably higher than the maximum number the count will ever reach. The lower figure is 2 rather than 0 to allow for a small amount of overshoot when the owl stops its second set of somersaults.

Of course, the rotation sensor will detect any overshoot, so readings from it could be used to control the motor and counteract the overshoot. However, in a simple application such as this it is probably not worthwhile bothering with this. Once the count goes below 2 the program moves on, and an Off instruction switches off the motor. The program then terminates.

Spirit.OCX version

This is the Spirit.OCX version of the Hootbot program, and it is almost a direct equivalent of the version in RCX code:

```
Private Sub Command1_Click()
With Spirit1
.InitComm
.SelectPrgm 0
.BeginOfTask 0
.SetSensorType 0, 4
.SetSensorType 2, 3
.SetPower "0", 2, 2
.Loop 2, 0
.SetVar 1, 9, 2
.SubVar 1, 2, 5
.While 9, 2, 0, 0, 1
.EndWhile
.PlayTone 1000, 30
.PlayTone 1300, 10
.PlayTone 990, 20
.PlayTone 900, 20
.PlayTone 890, 30
.PlayTone 880, 30
.PlayTone 870, 40
.SetFwd "0"
.While 9, 0, 1, 2, 240
.On "0"
```

```
.EndWhile
.Off "0"
.Wait 2, 100
.PlayTone 1000, 30
.PlayTone 1300, 10
.PlayTone 990, 20
.PlayTone 900, 20
.PlayTone 890, 30
.PlayTone 880, 30
.PlayTone 870, 40
.SetRwd "0"
.While 9, 0, 0, 2, 2
.On "0"
.EndWhile
.Off "0"
.EndLoop
.EndOfTask
End With
End Sub


Private Sub Command2_Click()
Spirit1.CloseComm
End
End Sub
```

The initial part of the program does the usual initialisation, including setting the relevant inputs to operate with the appropriate sensor type. The default sensor mode settings are satisfactory, so no SetSensorMode instructions are required. An infinite loop is used for the main program, and the owl will therefore go through its routine for as long as the light level remains below the selected threshold setting. The idea of this program is for the sensor to detect a shadow falling over the owl, so that the routine is performed when someone goes near it. Leave out the Loop and EndLoop instructions if you would prefer the unit to halt once the owl has performed its routine.

The reduction in light level is detected by taking an initial reading from the light sensor and then placing this in variable 1. Then five is deducted from the value in variable 1, and a While instruction repeatedly checks the value read from the light sensor against this value. This provides a hold-off while the reading from the sensor is higher than the value stored in the variable. The program moves on once a reading equal to or less than the stored value is obtained. Increase the value deducted from the initial reading to reduce the sensitivity of the unit, or decrease this value to boost sensitivity.

In other respects the program is much the same as the RCX code version. The sound effect is provided by two sets of PlayTone commands, but it would presumably be possible to put one set of commands into a subroutine and then call this routine at the relevant points in the program. However, as the effect is only used twice it is probably easier to use the method shown in the listing, with the copy and paste facility being used to add the second group of commands.

Tricks

The owl toy could actually be implemented using a touch switch rather than a rotation sensor to count the rotations. However, a rotation sensor is vastly more versatile than a touch switch for this type of thing. A touch switch can detect when a mechanism reaches a certain point, but it can only handle that one point. If you wish to know when the mechanism passes through several points, several touch switches will be required. With some step-up gearing a single rotation sensor can detect dozens or even hundreds of positions. This often enables changes in the way a robot functions to be implemented by modifying the software, with little or no alterations to the hardware being required.

The RCX code of Figure 7.39 gets the owl to start a somersault, but it does not quite make it all the way round. After some backtracking, a few "beeps", and a second attempt it does finally make it all the way round to complete the somersault. As in the original Hootbot program, a hold-off is provided until the light sensor detects a suitably low light level. A short beep is then produced, the motor is set for forward operation, and the motor is switched on. A wait until block then halts progress until the count from the rotation sensor reaches 60, which means that the somersault is 75 percent complete.

Remember that due to the step-up gearing the count increments by 80 per complete revolution. Another "beep" is then produced and the direction of the motor is reversed. A second wait until block then halts progress until the count from the rotation sensor has reduced to 20, which occurs when the owl has gone back by half a somersault. Next another "beep" is produced, and the motor is set to forward operation again. A third wait until block then provides another hold-off, this time until the count has incremented to 80 and the somersault has been completed.

The precision of the rotation sensor enables the owl to be taken through any desired set of rotations and partial rotations. This is a

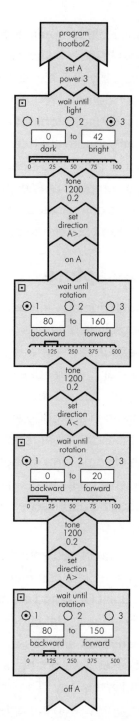

Fig.7.39 The alternative Hootbot code

rather frivolous application, but the rotation sensor is equally useful and versatile in more serious applications, such as in the steering mechanism of a vehicle. If you make the sound sensor you might like to try using this to trigger Hootbot. You could, for example, have Hootbot do one somersault per hand clap. Hootbot could be made more pet-like by programming it to randomly ignore the hand claps, or to shut down altogether and sulk once a certain number had been completed! It can also be made to go through quite a complex routine, perhaps with a random element or elements added. The more complicated and sophisticated the software, the more entertaining and lifelike your virtual pet is likely to be.

Data capture

Although primarily intended for use with robots, the RCX unit and the infrared tower provide a means of using a PC for measuring applications. The Lego temperature sensor was probably designed primarily for this type of thing rather than general use in robotics. One way of handling data capture is to simply use the PC to read data from the RCX unit and then display it directly on screen in analogue and (or) digital format. The alternative is to read data from the RCX unit at regular intervals and store it for later use, display it as a graph of some form, or both. Manipulating large amounts of data in this way is known as data logging incidentally. Here we will consider both the direct and logging approaches to handling data, starting with the direct display of data.

Data is transferred from the RCX unit to the PC using the Poll command. This is an immediate command that runs in Visual BASIC (or whatever) with the aid of Spirit.OCX, and it is not downloaded to the RCX unit. The Poll command simply requests data from the RCX unit, which it then provides via the infrared link. The RCX unit does not have to be running a program at the time, and in most cases it will not be running any software other than the firmware when it is used in this way. The Poll command is effectively used as a variable within Visual BASIC, and the data from this command is normally placed into a true variable where it can be manipulated in the desired fashion.

Thermometer

As an example of how data can be read from the RCX unit and used in Visual BASIC programs we will consider a simple thermometer program that provides both analogue and digital readouts. This requires the form to be increased from its default size so that it can accommodate everything, but this is just a matter of using the mouse to drag the bottom left-hand corner of the form until it is the required size. The form has three command buttons placed towards the bottom of the screen and well over to the left. Command buttons 1 to 3 are respectively captioned START, STOP, and END. A timer component is added anywhere on the form where it will be out of the way. The timer's interval property governs the frequency at which readings are taken, and a value of 250 (every 250ms or four times per second) is suitable.

A label component is added above the command buttons, and this is used to provide the digital readout. I would suggest that the font property is adjusted to give a large font size of about 24 point so that the readout is easy to see. The AutoSize property should be set to Auto. The size of the label will then be adjusted so that it is always just large enough for the text it contains. Of course, Spirit.OCX must also be added to the form.

The analogue display is provided by a line component, and initially a short vertical line is drawn anywhere in the bottom right-hand section of the screen. With the line component selected, the Properties window is used to "fine tune" its characteristics. Use these co-ordinates for the line:

X1   5880

X2   5880

Y1   4920

Y2   4500

The line is widened by setting the BorderWidth to 15, and the BorderStyle should be set to 1-Solid if it is not already at this setting. The BorderColor should be set to red, so that the line resembles the column of alcohol in a conventional alcohol thermometer. A circular shape object can be added at

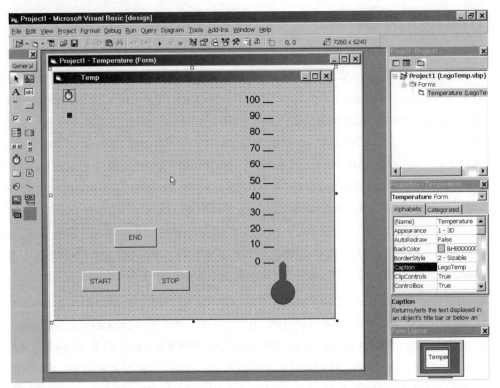

Fig.7.40 Screen dump showing the form for the thermometer program

the bottom of the line and set to the same colour as the line. This represents the bulb of alcohol in our virtual thermometer. Further line and label components can be added above the line to act as a scale.

The top of the line is currently at the 0 degree Celsius mark, and this is just its starting point. When the program is run, the line will grow upwards to provide the appropriate reading. It moves up the screen by 40 co-ordinate points per degree Celsius, but the co-ordinate system used in Visual BASIC has the maximum Y value at the bottom of the screen and the minimum Y value at the bottom. Lines representing 10-degree divisions therefore run from a Y value of 4500 at 0 degrees to 500 at 100 degrees.

Figure 7.40 shows a Visual BASIC screen dump that includes the completed form, and Figure 7.41 shows the finished program in operation. Obviously everything does not have to be laid out in exactly the same fashion as the prototype software, but it is advisable to follow it quite closely unless you are an experienced programmer.

This is the Visual BASIC listing for the thermometer program:

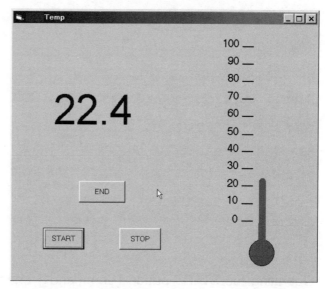

Fig.7.41 The thermometer program in operation

```
Private Sub
Command1_Click()
Timer1.Enabled =
True
End Sub


Private Sub Command2_Click()
Timer1.Enabled = False
End Sub


Private Sub Command3_Click()
Spirit1.CloseComm
End
End Sub


Private Sub Form_Load()
Spirit1.InitComm
Spirit1.SetSensorType 0, 2
Spirit1.SetSensorMode 0, 5, 0
End Sub
```

```
Private Sub Timer1_Timer()
Reading = Spirit1.Poll(9, 0)
Reading = Reading / 10
Label1.Caption = Reading
Reading = Reading * 40
Reading = Reading + 500
Reading = 5000 - Reading
Line1.Y2 = Reading
End Sub
```

Operating the START button (Command1) enables Timer1 and starts the program running. If the STOP button (Command2) is operated the timer is disabled, effectively halting the program and freezing the display with the last reading. Operating the START button again resumes normal operation, and these two buttons can be used to stop and start the program as often as you like. Operating the END button (Command3) closes communications with the infrared tower and terminates the program. The code assigned to the form simply initialises communications with the infrared tower and sets the Sensor mode and type. The SensorType command sets input 1 of the RCX unit to operate with a temperature sensor and the SensorMode instruction sets this input to the degrees Celsius mode. If you do not have the temperature sensor you can try out the program with another type of analogue sensor, such as the light type, by modifying these two commands. The mathematics elsewhere in the program might also need some modifications if you try this.

The main program is assigned to the timer. First this uses the Poll command to read the temperature sensor and place the result in the variable called Reading. On the face of it, there should be no problem if this variable is then displayed on the label to provide the digital readout. In practice there is a very minor problem in that a reading that appears as (say) 21.2 degrees on the RCX unit's display will actually be read from the RCX unit as a value of 212. The integer stored in Reading is therefore divided by 10 before it is assigned to the caption of Label1.

The value stored in Reading now has to be manipulated to provide a suitable Y2 co-ordinate for Line1, which provides the analogue display. As pointed out previously, each degree Celsius corresponds to 40 in the co-ordinate system, so Reading is first multiplied by 40. The top of the line is at a Y2 co-ordinate 500 at maximum reading, and not zero, so 500 is added to the value in Reading to allow for this offset. This gives a range of values from 500 at 0 degrees to 4500 at 100 degrees, but the co-ordinate system requires things the other way round. The inversion is easily achieved, and it is just a matter of deducting the value stored in Reading from 5000. This gives the final value for the Y2 co-ordinate, which can then be applied to Line1.

As this program demonstrates, Visual BASIC is well suited to providing large digital readouts and analogue style displays. With early BASIC programming languages this type of thing always seemed to involve hours of programming, but with Visual BASIC it can be achieved using a minimal amount of conventional programming.

Data logging

Data logging is not that different to the direct method described previously, but existing readings are stored in some way rather than simply being discarded when a new reading is taken. One way of handling things is to place each new reading into its own variable. Computing languages such as Visual BASIC have facilities to simplify the handling of large amounts of data, and arrays are the most important of these. An array is simply a block of variables that have the same name, together with a different number to give each one a separate identity. To try out reading data into an array load Spirit.OCX, two timer components, and a label component onto a form (Figure 7.42). Timer1 has an interval setting of 1000 and that for Timer2 is set at 500. Timer1 is left with its default Enabled setting, but for Timer2 this should be set to False. Set a large font size of about 24 for label1, and set the AutoSize parameter to Enabled. The listing for the data logging program is provided overleaf:

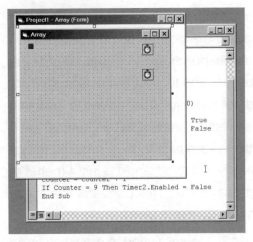

Fig.7.42 The form for the data logging program

```
Dim Readings(9) As Integer
Dim Counter As Integer
Private Sub Form_Load()
Spirit1.InitComm
Spirit1.SetSensorType 0, 3
Counter = 0
End Sub

Private Sub Timer1_Timer()
Readings(Counter) =
Spirit1.Poll(9, 0)
Counter = Counter + 1
If Counter = 9 Then Timer2.Enabled = True
If Counter = 9 Then Timer1.Enabled = False
If Counter = 9 Then Counter = 0
End Sub
Private Sub Timer2_Timer()
Label1.Caption = Readings(Counter)
Counter = Counter + 1
If Counter = 9 Then Timer2.Enabled = False
End Sub
```

All the program does is to take 10 readings at one-second intervals, and then display each of the readings, in turn, on Label1 for 0.5 seconds. The first two lines of the program are outside any of the subroutines, and they respectively declare the array and a variable. Variables and arrays can be either "private" or "public" when using Visual BASIC. If an array or variable is declared or first used inside a subroutine, it will only be recognised within that subroutine, and it is classed as private. By declaring the variable and the array outside any subroutines we are ensuring that they will be recognised by any code in the program, and that they are classed as public. Counter is just a simple variable that is used, as one would probably guess, as a counter. It is used as part of the routine that controls the number of readings that are taken. The array is called Readings, and the figure in parentheses that follows it determines the number of elements in the array. The numbering starts from zero though, so the value of 9 used in this case does actually give 10 elements numbered from 0 to 9.

When the program is run, the code assigned to the form starts things rolling by initialising communication with the infrared tower and setting the sensor type. The program sets input 1 of the RCX unit to operate with a light sensor in the default (percentage) mode, but this can obviously be altered if necessary. The value stored in Counter is set at an initial value of zero.

The readings are taken and stored by the code assigned to Timer1. This reads the sensor and places the value in Readings, and the first time it places the returned value in Readings(0). The zero here is provided by the initial value stored in Counter. Counter is then incremented by one, so that the next time a reading is taken the result is placed in Readings(1). The reading and storing process continues until Counter reaches a value of nine. The three If...Then statements then come into operation, and the first of these activates Timer2. The next switches off Timer1, and then the third resets Counter to zero.

Timer1 does not take any further part in the proceedings and control of the program is switched to Timer2. This displays the first reading via Label1 and then increments the value stored in Counter by one. The next time through it is therefore the second reading that is displayed, and then Counter is incremented again. The If...Then statement disables Timer2 once all 10 readings have been displayed and the value in Counter has reached 9 once again. At this point the program is effectively halted, with the final reading left on view via Label1 (Figure 7.43).

This program simply stores some results and then proves that they are stored safely and soundly by displaying them. Once a set of readings has been placed in an array it is possible to manipulate the data in a variety of ways using standard programming techniques. The software can be designed to search for and display maximum and minimum values, work out various types of mean reading, and so on. This program took only ten readings, but hundreds or even thousands of readings can be taken and stored. Also, readings can be taken over a much longer time span.

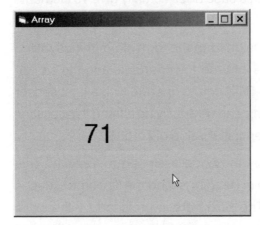

Fig.7.43 *The fully run program*

Graphing

The stored data can also be presented using various types of graph or chart, or readings can simply be dumped straight into a graphical form if preferred. To try out a graphing program go into Visual BASIC and drag the blank form to about double or so its original size on both dimensions. Add Spirit.OCX, a timer component, and a command button. The timer's Enabled parameter is set to False, and the Interval property is set at 250. Place the command button well towards the bottom of the screen and change its caption to START.

Much of the form is used for the graph. The bottom left-hand corner of the graphing area is at X and Y co-ordinates of 1200 and 4000 respectively. The top right-hand corner is at X and Y co-ordinates of 7200 and 1000. As a minimum it is advisable to draw two lines to represent the primary X and Y axes, but it is also well worthwhile adding X and Y calibration points plus some labels. It is then much easier to interpret results from the graph. The Y scaling runs from 4000 at the bottom to 1000 at the top, giving a range of 3000. Readings from the RCX unit run from 0 to 100, so each increment by one from the RCX unit corresponds to 30 in the co-ordinate system. I would

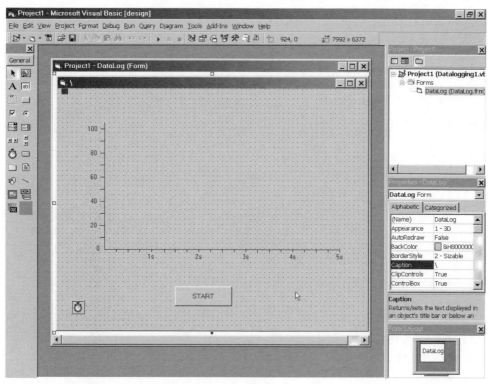

Fig.7.44 The form for the graphing program

suggest adding calibration ticks at 10 unit intervals, or every 300 co-ordinate units up the Y-axis in other words.

The X scaling runs from 1200 to 7200, which represents a range of 6000 co-ordinate points. This range corresponds to five seconds, which works out at 1200 per second, or 300 per 250-millisecond increment. There is plenty of space for a calibration tick at each 250-millisecond interval along the X-axis.

Once the screen design is complete you should have something like the screen shown in Figure 7.44. This is the Visual BASIC listing for the graphing program:

```
Dim Graphl As Integer
Dim Tm As Integer
```

```
Private Sub Command1_Click()
Timer1.Enabled = True
Graphl = Spirit1.Poll(9, 0)
Graphl = Graphl * 30
Graphl = 4000 - Graphl
Tm = 1200

End Sub

Private Sub Form_Load()
Spirit1.InitComm
Spirit1.SetSensorType 0, 3
End Sub
Private Sub Label12_Click()
End Sub

Private Sub Timer1_Timer()
Tm2 = Tm
Tm = Tm + 300
Graphr = Spirit1.Poll(9, 0)
Graphr = Graphr * 30
Graphr = 4000 - Graphr
Line (Tm2, Graphl)-(Tm, Graphr)
Graphl = Graphr
If Tm = 7200 Then Timer1.Enabled = False
End Sub
```

The program starts by declaring Graphl and Tm as public variables, and they are both set as integers. The code assigned to the form initialises communication with the infrared tower and sets input 1 of the RCX unit for operation with a light sensor. The default sensor mode (percentage) is used, so no SetSensorMode command is required.

When the START button is operated Timer1 is enabled, and an initial reading is taken and placed in the variable called Graphl, which is used to store the Y1 co-ordinate each time a new section of the graph is added. The value stored in Graphl is multiplied by 30 and then deducted from 4000 to get the scaling right for the Visual BASIC co-ordinate system and the screen area we are using. Finally, variable Tm (Time) is set at an initial value of 1200. This variable supplies the X2 co-ordinate each time a new segment of the graph is drawn. It might seem that the reading taken when the START button is pressed would simply duplicate the first reading taken by Timer1. However, this is not the case, because the code assigned to a timer is not performed when the timer is enabled. The code is not performed until the appropriate time has elapsed, which in this case is 250 milliseconds later.

When the timer's code is run it starts by placing the value stored in Tm into Tm2. The latter is used as the X1 co-ordinate when a new section of the graph is drawn. We now have the X1 (Tm2) and Y1 (Graphl) co-ordinates, but require the X2 and Y2 data before the first segment of the graph can be drawn. Simply adding 300 to Tm gives it the correct value for the X2 co-ordinate. To obtain the Y2 co-ordinate another reading is taken, the returned value is multiplied by 30, and then it is deducted from 4000. This value is stored in the variable called Graphr. With all four co-ordinates now stored in variables, the first segment of the graph is drawn using a Line command.

What are currently the X2 and Y2 co-ordinates will be used as the X1 and Y1 co-ordinates when the next section of the graph is produced. The value in Graphr is therefore placed in Graphl. The value in Tm is copied to Tm2 at the beginning of the routine the next time the timer code is performed. The value in Tm is then incremented by 300 again to provide the new X2 value, and a new reading is taken and processed to provide the new Y2 value. Another

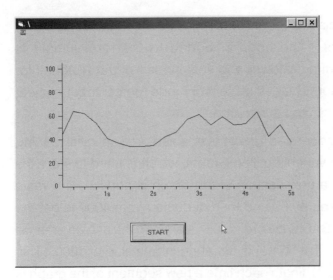

Fig.7.45 A graph produced by the program

segment of the graph is then drawn, and so on until the complete graph has been produced. Things are halted when the If...Then statement detects that Tm has reached a value of 7200, which means that the graph has been completed. Timer1 is then switched off, effectively halting the program. However, the graph will still be left on the screen so that it can be examined. Figure 7.45 shows an example graph produced using this program. In order to close the program left-click on the cross in the top right-hand corner of the window.

This program is easily modified for operation with a different sensor or to take more samples. The sampling rate is controlled by Timer1's Interval property, and is easily changed as well. There is plenty of scope for customising and extending this software.

Extra motor

Additional sensors, whether home constructed or the Lego "real thing", greatly extend the scope of the Robotics Invention System. It is a mistake to overlook the other side of things though. The RCX unit has three outputs but the Robotics Invention System is supplied with just two motors. An extra motor is at least as useful as an additional sensor, and many would ague that it is the most useful add-on for the standard kit. An extra motor certainly extends the range of possibilities. A robot vehicle requires two motors if it is to have proper steering. Either one motor is used to provide propulsion while the other operates the steering mechanism, or the two motors power wheels or tracks on opposite sides of the vehicle. Either way, there is no motor left to operate any additional gadget, such as a grabbing or lifting mechanism.

It is possible to compromise on the method of steering used, with the vehicle turning one way when it is set into reverse, but this gives rather crude and limited control. Using an extra motor is a much better way of doing things, and an extra motor is well worth the cost involved. Incidentally, there is more than one type of Lego motor available. The reduction gear variety, as supplied with the Robotics Invention System, is the most useful for our purposes, and is the only one we will consider here.

Crabbot

No, Crabbot does not walk sideways! Its name is derived from the crab-like claws at the front (Figures 7.46 and 7.47). These enable small objects to be grabbed and moved around by the robot. This robot is basically the same as the rover style robot used in previous chapters, but the RCX unit is mounted sideways and the front-end is modified slightly to accommodate the additional mechanism. Like the robot it is based on, Crabbot has forward and reverse control, plus full steering control provided by separate motors driving the main wheels. The claws are opened and closed using a third motor. This additional motor is the only item required that is not part of the standard Robotics Invention System. The claw mechanism can potentially be used with other rover style robots, or as part of a robot arm.

Fig.7.46 Crabbot's claws

Fig.7.47 The finished Crabbot. An extra motor is needed to build this robot

Fig.7.48 The RCX unit is mounted across the chassis

Step 1 (Figures 7.48 to 7.50)

The rear section of the robot is exactly the same as that of the rover style robot used in previous chapters. The middle section differs only in that the RCX unit is mounted across the chassis, as can be seen from Figure 7.48. The RCX unit is wired to the motors in exactly the same fashion as in the original design. The front of the robot has been substantially modified to give a large clear area that acts as a mounting pad for the claw assembly (Figure 7.49). The easiest way to build the front section is to initially just fit five plates on the front platform (Figure 7.50). These will eventually act as a mounting pad for the claw assembly. The front wheel assembly is then built as a separate module, which is not added to the main unit until it has been completed.

Fig.7.49 The platform for the claw mechanism

Step 2 (Figures 7.51 to 7.53)

The chassis for the front wheel assembly has two side pieces that are each based on two 8 by 1 beams. These are joined together using four 8 by 1 plates, and a 4 by 1 beam is sandwiched between one pair of these plates. An 8 by 2 plate is added on top of the chassis and another is fitted on the underside. These plates must be of the type that

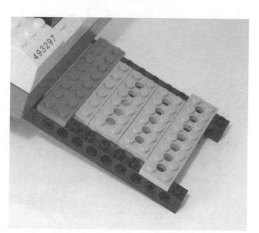

Fig.7.50 The first stage of building the front section

has holes, because the front wheel assembly is mounted via two of these holes. Figures 7.51 and 7.52 show top and bottom views of this assembly. Next a 6 by 1 beam is added on top of the chassis, and a 6 by 1 plate is fitted on top of this. The front wheel assembly is then mounted on the two 8 by 2 plates. The front wheel unit only differs from the original in that it uses a 63-millimetre shaft instead of a 79-millimetre type. Figure 7.53 shows the

Fig.7.51 Top view of the platform

Fig.7.52 The underside of the front wheel platform

Fig.7.53 The completed front wheel assembly

completed front wheel assembly, which is ready to be fitted to the underside of the main unit.

Step 3 (Figures 7.54 and 7.55)

Construction of the claw assembly starts with the platform that forms the basis of the unit. This consists of four 12 by 1 beams and one 6 by 1 beam that are held together using black pegs. Figure 7.54 shows the platform with the beams pulled apart slightly to show the pegs. To complete the platform it is fitted with two 4 by 2 plates and a single 4 by 1 plate (Figure 7.55).

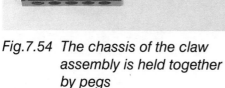

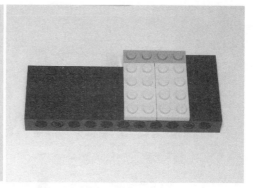

Fig.7.54 The chassis of the claw assembly is held together by pegs

Fig.7.55 The plates added to the chassis

Step 4 (Figures 7.56 to 7.61)

Next the claw mechanism is assembled and fitted to the platform. The parts for one of the claws are shown in Figure 7.56. The other claw uses the same parts except the shaft for the second one is 63 millimetres long instead of 47 millimetres. The finished claws are shown in Figure 7.57. A peg is used to fit each pair of angled beams together, and then the shafts are fitted. Finally, the 16-tooth gearwheels are added onto the shafts. A mounting bracket for the claws is made from four 4 by 1 beams and two 4 by 2 angle plates (Figure 7.58). The two claws are then added onto the bracket (Figure 7.59), making sure that the two

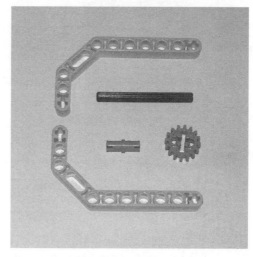

Fig.7.56 The parts for one claw

gearwheels mesh properly, and that the claws are reasonably symmetrical. Two pulleys of the smallest size are used to fix the claws in place. A 40-tooth

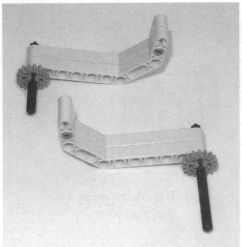

Fig.7.57 The two assembled claws

Fig.7.58 The assembly used to fit
the claws onto the platform

Fig.7.59 The claws fitted onto the
mounting bracket

Fig.7.60 The claws ready to be
fitted on the chassis

gearwheel is added onto the longer shaft to complete the assembly (Figure 7.60) which is then added to the platform (Figure 7.61).

Fig.7.61 The completed claw assembly ready for installation

Step 5 (Figure 7.62 and 7.63)

Next the motor is fitted at the rear of the claw mechanism. First a mounting pad is added using two 2 by 1 plates and a single 2 by 2 type (Figure 7.62). The motor is fitted with an 8-tooth gearwheel and then it is fitted onto the pad (Figure 7.63).

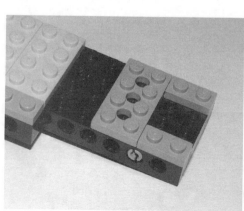

Fig.7.62 The mounting pad for the motor

Fig.7.63 The motor fitted onto the mounting pad

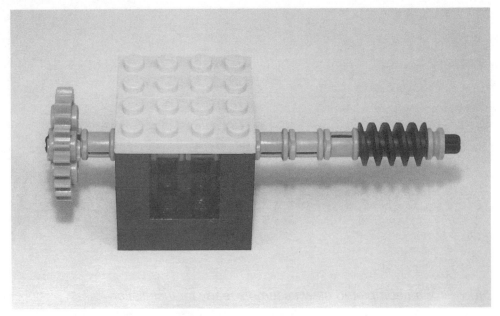

Fig.7.64 The worm drive assembly that drives the claws

Step 6 (Figure 7.64 to 7.68)

The motor is linked to the claw mechanism by way of a worm drive assembly
(Figure 7.64). Assembly starts with two 4 by 2 bricks that are joined by fitting
two 4 by 1 beams on top of them. A further 4 by 1 beam is then placed on top

*Fig.7.65 The chassis for the
worm drive*

*Fig.7.66 The drive shaft and
its associated parts*

of each of these beams (Figure 7.65). The parts shown in Figure 7.66 are then added to produce the assembly of Figure 7.67. To complete the worm drive a couple of 4 by 2 plates are added across the tops of the beams to give additional strength. The worm drive is then added to the main

Fig.7.67 The completed drive shaft assembly

unit (Figure 7.68). There is a 3 to 1 reduction ratio from the motor to the worm gear, and then a 40 to 1 reduction from the worm gear to the gearwheel that drives the claws. This gives a total reduction ratio of 120 to 1, which ensures that the claws are operated in a controlled manner, rather than snapping shut and flying open.

Fig.7.68 The completed claw mechanism, ready for installation

Fig.7.69 The claw mechanism installed on the robot

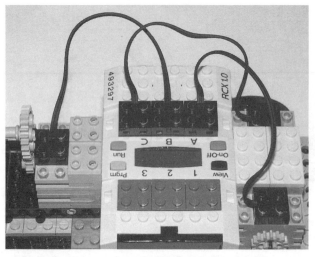

Fig.7.70 The connections to the RCX unit

Step 7 (Figures 7.69 to 7.72)

The completed claw assembly is now fitted onto the front of the vehicle (Figure 7.69) and it is connected to output B of the RCX unit (Figure 7.70). This gives the completed robot of Figures 7.71 and 7.72.

Fig.7.71 The completed Crabbot ready for action

Figure 7.72 Another view of the completed Crabbot robot

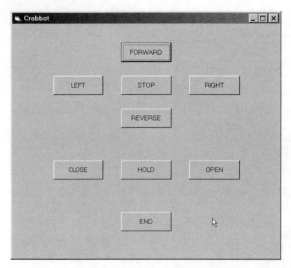

Fig.7.73 The Crabbot control panel

Crabbot software

One way of using Crabbot is with an additional sensor or sensors, and built-in software to enable it to seek out something and grab hold of it. A tennis ball or something of a similar size should make a suitable target object. The alternative, and the one we will explore here, is to use Crabbot in the direct mode, with manual control via an onscreen control panel. The Crabbot software requires a form equipped with Spirit.OCX and nine command buttons, as in Figure 7.73, which shows the program in action. The captions for the buttons can be seen from this. The form will have to be dragged to a larger size in order to provide enough space for the buttons. With only one or two buttons I do not normally bother renaming them, but with nine to contend with it is advisable to rename the buttons to match their captions. It is then obvious which code is applied to which button. This is the Visual BASIC listing for the Crabbot software.

```
Private Sub Close_Click()
Spirit1.On "1"
Spirit1.SetRwd "1"
End Sub

Private Sub End_Click()
Spirit1.Off "012"
Spirit1.CloseComm
```

```
End
End Sub


Private Sub Form_Load()
Spirit1.InitComm
Spirit1.PBTxPower 1
End Sub


Private Sub Forward_Click()
Spirit1.On "02"
Spirit1.SetFwd "02"
End Sub


Private Sub Hold_Click()
Spirit1.Off "1"
End Sub


Private Sub Left_Click()
Spirit1.On "02"
Spirit1.SetFwd "2"
Spirit1.SetRwd "0"
End Sub


Private Sub Open_Click()
Spirit1.On "1"
Spirit1.SetFwd "1"
End Sub
```

```
Private Sub Reverse_Click()
Spirit1.On "02"
Spirit1.SetRwd "02"
End Sub


Private Sub Right_Click()
Spirit1.On "02"
Spirit1.SetFwd "0"
Spirit1.SetRwd "2"
End Sub


Private Sub Stop_Click()
Spirit1.Off "02"
End Sub
```

Communication with the RCX unit is initialised when the form loads, and the RCX unit's infrared transmitter is set at high power by the PBTxPower command. The power setting switch on the infrared tower must also be set for long range operation. Operating the END button switches off all three motors, closes communication with the infrared tower, and terminates the program. The various other buttons simply issue the appropriate motor control commands to provide the desired action. For example, motors 0 and 2 are set for forward operation and switched on in order to make Crabbot go forward and motor 1 is set to go in reverse to close the claws. Learning to control a robot via the infrared link takes a little practice. There is a slight delay between a control being operated and the robot responding, but the time lag is only a fraction of a second. Even so, you have to learn to compensate for this when making very fine adjustments to the robot's position or the claws.

Armbot

Robot arms are something that most robotics enthusiasts find particularly interesting, but with just two motors in the Robotics Invention System only a limited range of control can be provided. Adding a third motor improves matters considerably, although it is only fair to point out that a robot arm should ideally have at least four motors. On the face of it, three motors are sufficient to give a very basic version of a human arm and hand. One motor opens and closes the robot equivalent of a hand, while the other two operate the equivalents of the shoulder and elbow joints. Such an arrangement enables

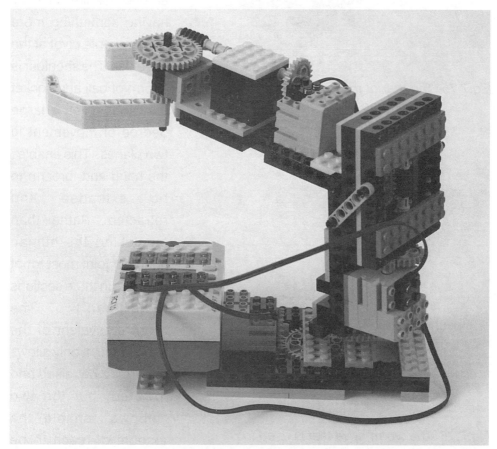

Fig.7.74 Armbot uses three motors, one more than is supplied as standard in the Robotics Invention System

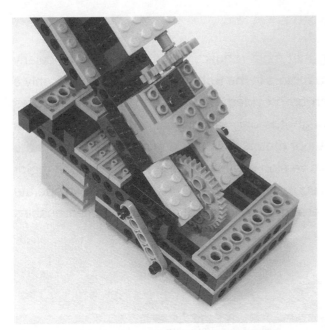

Fig.7.75 *The rear of the claw mechanism is extended to accommodate the gearwheel that drives the arm*

Fig.7.76 *The worm drive that is used to raise and lower the arm*

the robot to grasp objects, which can then be lifted. The whole arm can be rotated so that the object can be released somewhere else.

The problem is that there is no way of controlling how far the arm reaches. The human arm gets around this limitation by having something more than a simple pivot at the shoulder. The shoulder is a form of ball and socket joint that gives a large degree of movement in two planes. This enables the hand and forearm to be extended and retracted. Rather than mimicking the human shoulder joint most robot arms are in three sections rather than two. The robot equivalent of the shoulder joint only allows the arm to be raised and lowered, but the two "elbows" enable the amount of reach to be controlled.

Although a simple two section Lego robot arm such as the one shown in Figure 7.74 provides something less than complete control, it is nevertheless an interesting robot for the experimenter. The "hand" and "forearm" are based on the claw assembly of Crabbot. As can be seen from Figure 7.75, pegging a couple of 8 by 1 beams in place extends the rear of this assembly. A couple of green 2 by 1 bricks are held in place at the rear of the beams using pairs of 2 by 2 and 2 by 4 plates. A shaft passes through these holes and carries a 40-tooth gearwheel. The holes in the green bricks lock the shaft to the claw mechanism, and it can therefore be raised or lowered by driving the 40-tooth gearwheel.

Fig.7.77 Another view of the worm drive that raises and lowers the arm

The drive to this gearwheel is via a worm gear using an arrangement that is similar to the one that is used to open and close the claws. Figures 7.76 and 7.77 show two views of this section of the robot. Each side is based on a 12 by 1 beam and a 10 by 1 type. Various beams and plates hold the two sides together, with a six unit wide gap between them. Two of the crossbeams provide the mounting for the worm drive. The bottom end of the arm assembly is fitted with a shaft and a 40-tooth gearwheel. The drive that rotates the arm is applied to this gearwheel. The shaft must be locked to the arm assembly, and this is achieved by including a green 2 by 1 brick at the bottom end of the arm.

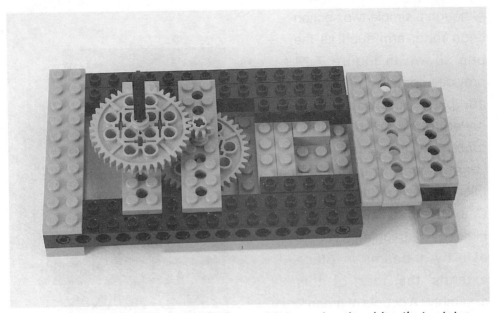

Fig.7.78 *Top view of the base section, which carries the drive that rotates the entire arm*

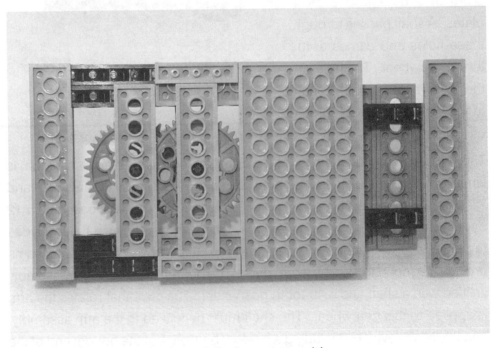

Fig.7.79 *The underside view of the base assembly*

Fig.7.80 The RCX unit and motor installed on the base unit

The base section carries the rest of the drive that rotates the whole arm. Figures 7.78 and 7.79 show the top and underside views. The sides are each made from two 16 by 1 beams pegged together, and two 10 by 1 beams pegged to the main side sections provide the extension that accommodates the RCX unit (Figure 7.80). Various plates hold the sides together and provide mountings for the drive shafts and gears. Ideally the rotation of the arm would be provided by a third worm drive. This would give a suitably high reduction ratio and resist any overshoot of the arm, giving very precise control. Unfortunately, the Robotics Invention System only includes two of these gears. Additional worm gears are available of course, and it would be interesting to obtain some and utilize a third for the arm rotation drive of this robot.

As things stand, the motor is fitted with a 24-tooth crown gear that drives an intermediate drive shaft via a 40-tooth gearwheel. An 8-tooth gearwheel on

Fig.7.81 The completed Armbot robot

the intermediate shaft drives the 40-tooth gearwheel on the arm. This gives a total reduction ratio of 8.3 to 1. This is quite a high reduction ratio, but is nothing like as high as the reduction used on the other sections of the arm. These have a 3 to 1 reduction followed by a 40 to 1 reduction, giving an overall ratio of 120 to 1. With an 8.3 to 1 reduction ratio the arm rotates fast enough to make control difficult and it is advisable to reduce the power to the relevant motor in order to slow things down to a more manageable level. This gives better control, but a certain amount of overshoot has to be expected.

Outputs A to C of the RCX unit are respectively used to drive the motor that raises and lowers the arm, the one that controls the claws, and the one that rotates the arm. An ordinary Lego connecting lead is suitable to make the connection to output C, but longer leads are needed for the other two connections. The Robotics Invention System includes two long leads that

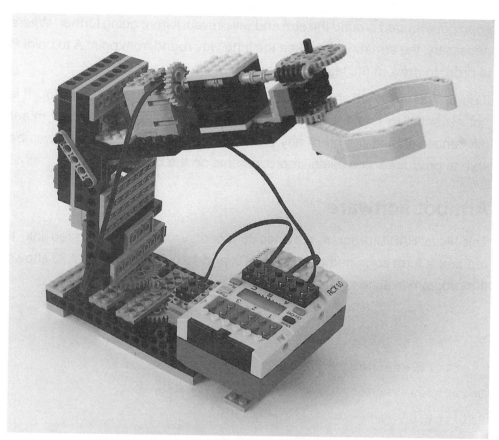

Fig.7.82 *Another view of the finished Armbot robot*

can be used, but these are very much longer than is really necessary. One alternative is to connect two short leads together to make a double length lead. Another option is to buy the longer leads that are available as an accessory pack. This pack contains three leads of different lengths, and the two shorter leads are ideal for this robot.

Incidentally, apart from the additional motor it is possible to build Armbot using nothing more than the standard kit of parts supplied in the Robotics Invention System. When using Armbot always bear in mind that the two leads from the RCX unit to the motors on the moving arm do impose restrictions. In particular, if the arm is always rotated in the same direction these leads will soon get wrapped around the arm and will prevent it from going further. Where necessary, the arm must be taken the long way round from point A to point B in order to prevent the leads from getting seriously tangled.

Figures 7.81 and 7.82 show two further views of the completed Armbot. It is not essential to make an exact clone of the prototype, and a few minor differences should not be of any practical consequence. You may well be able to produce some useful improvements on the basic design.

Armbot software

This Visual BASIC program provides control of Armbot via the infrared link. It requires a form equipped with Spirit.OCX and 10 buttons. Figure 7.83 shows the program in action.

```
Private Sub AntiClock_Click()
Spirit1.SetPower "2", 2, 1
Spirit1.SetFwd "2"
Spirit1.On "2"
End Sub


Private Sub ClockWise_Click()
Spirit1.SetPower "2", 2, 1
Spirit1.SetRwd "2"
Spirit1.On "2"
End Sub


Private Sub Close_Click()
Spirit1.On "1"
Spirit1.SetRwd "1"
End Sub
```

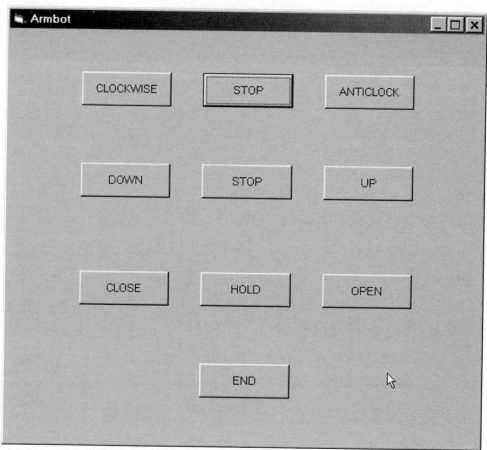

Fig.7.83 The Visual BASIC control panel for Armbot

```
Private Sub Down_Click()
Spirit1.SetFwd "0"
Spirit1.On "0"
End Sub

Private Sub End_Click()
Spirit1.Off "012"
Spirit1.CloseComm
```

```
      End
      End Sub


      Private Sub Form_Load()
      Spirit1.InitComm
      Spirit1.PBTxPower 1
      End Sub


      Private Sub Hold_Click()
      Spirit1.Off "1"
      End Sub


      Private Sub Open_Click()
      Spirit1.On "1"
      Spirit1.SetFwd "1"
      End Sub


      Private Sub Stop_Click()
      Spirit1.Off "2"
      End Sub
      Private Sub StopUD_Click()
      Spirit1.Off "0"
      End Sub


      Private Sub Up_Click()
      Spirit1.SetRwd "0"
      Spirit1.On "0"
      End Sub
```

The names of the command buttons have been changed to match their respective captions. The program operates in much the same manner as the Crabbot software, with the appropriate motor direction and (or) On/Off commands being assigned to each command button. If any parts of the arm go in the wrong direction when a button is operated, fitting the connector on the motor the other way round should correct things. When the form loads, the InitComm and PBTxPower commands are issued, and the END button closes communication with the tower and terminates the program.

One way of using Armbot is as a Lego alternative to the slot machines that have a remote controlled crane. The contestant tries to obtain some sort of reward by picking it up using the claws, and then depositing it in another container after some nifty manoeuvring of the arm. The reward can be something like a small chocolate bar, a sweet, or a small toy.

Like the "real thing", Armbot will probably exhibit an annoying tendency to drop the reward before you have a chance to position it over the second container. You can either accept this as part of the fun or try to improve Armbot's grip. There are some Lego odds and ends in the kit that might help, but something like some thin foam material is likely to be the most effective solution.

Having vision

I suppose that when it comes to the contest for the ultimate Lego MindStorms sensor it is strictly a case of "no contest". Although not exactly cheap, the Lego Vision Command system is undoubtedly the ultimate MindStorms accessory at present. It is basically just a small television camera, or webcam as this type of device is now usually called. The original function of these units was to enable low definition television pictures or still pictures to be sent over the Internet. The camera supplied as part of the Vision Command system can actually be used in this way, or with any webcam aware application, but its primary purpose is to enable Lego MindStorms robots to "see".

This is not a standard sensor that connects to an input of the RCX unit. Instead, it connects to the PC via a few metres of cable and a USB port. One advantage of this system is that the camera can be powered from the PC, making it unnecessary for the camera to draw power from the RCX unit or to have its own battery supply. The obvious drawback is that any robot fitted with the camera is tethered to the PC and lacks the freedom of movement enjoyed by self-contained robots. The degree of freedom is also less than that obtained with a robot that relies on the infrared link. However, the camera greatly extends the capabilities of the Robotics Invention System and its entertainment value. The lack of full mobility is a price that is well worth paying.

Onboard view

The software supplied with the Vision Command system enables the camera to be used on its own to detect specific colours or movement, and the area of coverage can be broken down into various preset patterns. When used in isolation the camera can be used to trigger sounds, take snapshots, or record snatches of video. The range of possibilities is relatively limited though, and the system works best in conjunction with the Robotics Invention System. Robots that utilize the Lego Cam are normally programmed using the software supplied with the Vision Command system and not using ordinary RCX code or visual BASIC. The software supplied with the system provides vision recognition and a programming environment that is very similar to the one used for RCX code. However, the commands available to control the robots are perhaps rather more generalised and less accommodating than standard RCX code or Visual BASIC plus Spirit.OCX.

One interesting way to use the camera is to fit it on a rover style robot, which is then controlled from the PC. The onboard camera is used to provide television pictures on the PC's monitor so that the robot can be driven properly without looking at the robot itself. You rely wholly on the feedback from the camera, which gives the view you would see if you were actually on the robot yourself. With this method it is not necessary to use the programming language provided with the Vision Command system, because the robot is controlled manually and is not automatically responding to the signal from the camera.

There is a slight problem with this approach in that the RCX code program and the main software supplied with the Vision Command system are not standard Windows programs. They are designed to run full-screen and can not be run side by side with other software. With this approach two programs must run simultaneously. One program is needed to control the robot and another provides the television picture.

The problem is by no means insurmountable, and manual control of the robot requires a Visual BASIC program rather than RCX code anyway. I do not normally bother to compile MindStorms programs to an .EXE file, but instead run them from within Visual BASIC. In this case though, it is probably best to compile the program and then run it independently of Visual BASIC. This keeps thing more simple and straightforward, and is especially important if you are using a PC that has only a modest amount of memory. It should avoid the dreaded error messages or the PC simply hanging up due to lack of memory. Satisfactory results will almost certainly be obtained if you have a version of Visual BASIC that can not compile the control program. Having run the program from within Visual BASIC using the Start With Full Compile option, Visual BASIC itself can be minimised to keep the amount of memory used as low as possible.

As explained previously, the Lego camera will work with any software that can accommodate a standard webcam, so any normal webcam software should be able to provide the television picture. There are actually some useful webcam programs supplied as part of the Vision Command system that do not run full-screen. One of these can be used to supply the television pictures. For example, if you select Camera Software from the main menu, a further menu gives additional options. Television pictures from the webcam will be provided if you select one of these options. Try selecting Create Animation for example. Of course, you do not have to create an animation, an Email, or whatever. You just run the program to provide the feedback from the camera. With the two programs running side by side you can control the robot from the Visual BASIC program, and the webcam software will provide the pictures even though it is not running in the active window.

Fig.7.84 Crabbot fitted with the Lego Cam

Fig.7.85 The camera is mounted via pegs that fit into the sides

Seebot

The Lego camera is easily added to the standard version of our rover robot or the Crabbot variant. If you have the third motor it is worth adding it to the Crabbot version, which has greater potential. The instructions provided here are for adding the camera to Crabbot, but exactly the same method can be used if the claw mechanism is omitted from the robot. Figure 7.84

shows Crabbot fitted with the Lego camera, turning it into what we will call Seebot. Seebot is based on an unmodified version of Crabbot, and construction therefore commences by building Crabbot, following the instructions provided earlier in this chapter.

To add the camera first fit four black pegs into the holes at the sides of the camera. Two pegs go into the bottom pair of holes, and the other two go in the set of holes two units further up the camera (Figure 7.85). Next two 4 by 1 plates are added on a side section of the chassis, one on top of the other, and a 4 by 1 beam is added on top of these. Two black pegs are then fitted, one in the side of the chassis and one in the 4 by 1 beam (Figure 7.86). This process is then repeated on the other side of the chassis. Finally, the camera is mounted on the chassis via two 16 by 1 beams and the pegs already fitted to the chassis and the camera (Figure 7.87).

Fig.7.86 Additional plates and beams are added to the chassis

Fig.7.87 The camera is mounted on the robot using two beams

The camera can be mounted quite high up, as on the prototype, or lower down if preferred. If the robot is fitted with the claw mechanism it is best to mount the camera quite high up to ensure that the claws and their drive system do not significantly obscure the camera's view. In common with most webcams, the Lego camera does not have automatic focusing. You

*Fig.7.88 The camera is focused using the
ring around the lens. The camera
appears here approximately life size*

therefore have to manually adjust the focusing to obtain a good compromise setting. Focusing is accomplished by turning the light grey ring around the lens (Figure 7.88) while monitoring the picture via the PC's monitor. The depth of field is generally quite high, so finding a good compromise should not be too difficult.

Driving a rover style robot using feedback from simple sensors such as light types can be quite difficult, but with the picture from the Lego camera you should be able to control Seebot with great precision. In fact after a little practice it will probably be easier to drive it using feedback from the camera, rather than looking at the robot itself. One advantage of using the onboard camera is that you have the controls and the picture information side by side on the screen, making it unnecessary to keep looking at the robot and then back at the screen again. Something you do have to keep in mind is that the robot is connected to the PC by way of the camera's USB cable. Check the limits imposed by the cable before you start operating Seebot, and then keep comfortably within those limits.

Colour sense

Once fitted with the camera, Seebot can of course be programmed using the Vision Command software. If you have built the version that is complete with the claw mechanism it is interesting to try programming Seebot to seek out and grasp something. A ball about the size of a tennis ball makes a good target object. The Vision Command software can use movement, light level, or colour to act as a stimulus. These all provide interesting possibilities, but colour is perhaps the most interesting and useful method. The software operates on the basis of breaking up the picture from the camera into various zones or regions, with each one having its

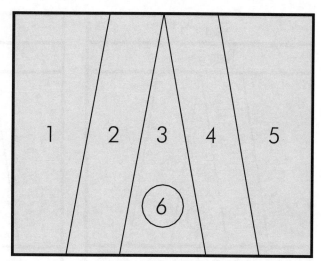

Fig.7.89 A number of different zoning patterns are available, but this is probably the best one for our purposes

own subprogram that is run when that area of the screen is activated. For our present purposes pattern number 16 (Figure 7.89) probably represents the best choice, but you might like to experiment with some of the others. For example, patterns 17 and 18 look quite useful for this application.

Each region of the screen has its own subprogram, which means that six of them are required in this case. Figure 7.90 shows the program for region 1, and the same routine is used for region 2. The routine for zone 3 is shown in Figure 7.91. Figure 7.92 shows the subprogram for zone 4, and the same routine is used for zone 5. Finally, Figure 7.93 shows the program for zone 6. This last one is slightly more difficult to enter than the others, because the motor control block requires a certain amount of "fine tuning".

If you right-click the mouse on this block a control panel will pop up on the screen, as represented by the large block in Figure 7.93. You can select which motor or motors are to be controlled, and by default they are all enabled. We only wish to control motor B, which is the one that controls the claw mechanism. Left-click on the squares for motors A and C at the top of the panel so that these motors are not affected. Then left-click on the arrowhead for motor B that points downward, which means that this motor will be set

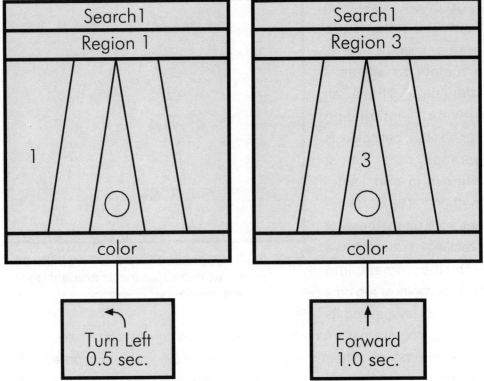

Fig.7.90 *The program for region 1 of the screen. The same program is used for region 2*

Fig.7.91 *The program for zone 3 of the screen*

into reverse when it is activated. Obviously the direction settings for the other two outputs are unimportant, as this command block will not switch them on. At the bottom of the panel a small dialogue box enables a time in seconds to be entered. This is the duration for which the motor will be switched on, and two seconds is a good starting point. Some fine adjustment will probably be needed in order to get things working just right.

In order to get the program to operate you must select the appropriate trigger colour for each part of the screen. In this case all regions of the screen are set to respond to the colour of the target object. This object must be predominantly one colour if the system is to stand a reasonable chance of working well. The built-in training system of the Vision Command kit explains how to show the software the colour it must recognise. This basically just entails holding the target object in front of the camera and operating the appropriate onscreen control button. Here we are trying to get the robot to home in on one object, so the same routine is used to set up each screen zone. In the Advanced settings there is a facility to make fine adjustments to the trigger colour, but this should not be necessary. The system responds to a range of colours rather than one specific colour, so it should not be difficult to get it to respond to the target object.

Under the Advanced settings it is also possible to adjust the sensitivity of each screen area. This operates on the basis of a threshold percentage being set.

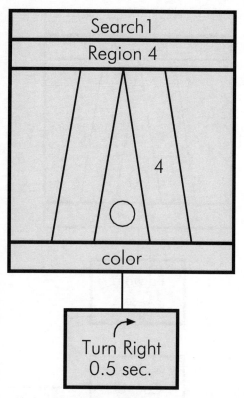

Fig.7.92 The program for screen zones 4 and 5

For example, the default sensitivity is 20, which means that at least 20 percent of that screen region must be the appropriate colour in order to activate the system. In general the default setting works quite well, but it can sometimes be advantageous to alter the setting. With this program I found that when the target object was in zone 6 but also spread into zone 3, it was often zone 3 that was activated, and not zone 6. Setting a higher value for the sensitivity parameter of zone 3 seems to avoid this problem, and a value of around 40 should give good results.

Program operation

The way in which the program operates is pretty straightforward. If the target object is detected in zones 1 or 2, the robot turns to the right in an attempt to

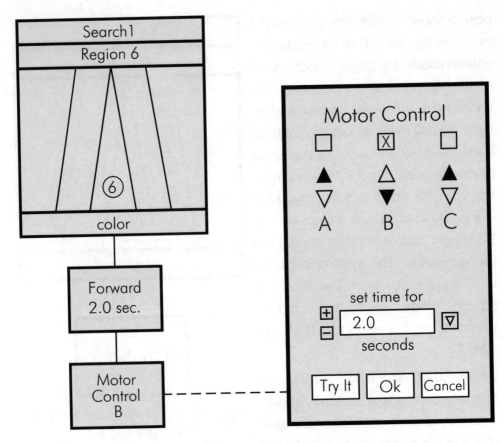

Fig.7.93 *The program for screen zone 6, including the motor control settings*

bring the object into the centre of the picture. With the target in region 4 or 5 the robot is turned to the left, again trying to bring it into the centre of the picture. Once in the centre the robot has been aimed at the object, but it might still be some distance away if the object is in zone 3. The robot is therefore moved forward if this zone is activated. Once into zone 6 the object is relatively close, but is still probably out of the reach of the claws. The robot is therefore moved forward and then the claws are closed.

You will probably need to do some "fine tuning" to the time settings used in the program, and the robot may still fail to home-in accurately enough on occasions, but it should at least get quite close. The obvious problem in an application of this type is that the camera does not give any range information, and to some extent the control software has to use the computer equivalent of guesswork.

When using the camera to detect colour you must always bear in mind that it works best with a fairly plain background having a colour that contrasts with that of the target object. With a complex background there is always a risk that something will be a similar colour to the target object, and that the system will become confused and throw a hi-tech wobbly. The software necessarily responds to a fairly broad colour range, so that any small changes in the lighting or the automatic exposure setting of the camera do not render it blind to the target object. This makes it important to keep anything of a similar colour to the target object out of the camera's field of view.

Ups and downs

The Vision Command programming language includes Tilt Up and Tilt Down commands, which are intended for use with a motorised camera mount. However, these commands control output B of the RCX unit and can be used with anything that is driven from this output. This includes the claw mechanism, where Tilt Up and Tilt Down respectively operate as Open Claws and Close Claws commands.

If you have an additional motor and the Vision Command system it is not difficult to fit our basic rover style robot with a motorised camera mount (Figure 7.94). It is then possible to aim the camera up or down in order to get a better look at things. Of course, it is not possible to use both the claws and a motorised camera mount, due to the three motor limitation of the RCX unit. Even if it does impose limitations elsewhere, it is still well worth experimenting with a motorised camera mount. The Vision Command system includes some extra plastic components that make it relatively easy to produce a mount of this type. In particular it includes a special block that takes a worm gear and a 24-tooth gearwheel, both of which are also supplied in the kit. Note that in order to build this version of Seebot you need the Vision Command system and an extra motor, but everything else used is part of the standard Robotics Invention System.

Fig.7.94 The finished robot, complete with camera drive

*Fig.7.95 The block and gears
for the drive*

*Fig.7.96 The base uses three
4 by 1 beams*

Step 1 (Figures 7.95 to 7.97)

The main robot is exactly the same as Crabbot, but the entire claw mechanism is omitted. Having built the basic Crabbot, the next step is to make the camera's drive assembly. This is based on the special block and gears mentioned previously (Figure 7.95). Three 4 by 1 beams are pegged together to form a base (Figure 7.96), and

Fig.7.97 *The block fitted on the base*

then a 4 by 2 plate is added on top of these. The block made from transparent plastic is then added on top of this, giving the assembly shown in Figure 7.97.

Step 2 (Figures 7.98 and 7.99)

To discourage the block from pulling free of the base section it is joined to it using a 5 by 1 beam (the type that has rounded ends and holes right through). This is fitted with a normal peg at one end, and the shorter type at the other

Fig.7.98 *The beam fitted with the two pegs*

Fig.7.99 *The beam installed on the base section*

end (Figure 7.98). This assembly is then added to the main assembly (Figure 7.99). The peg with the short fitting goes into the plastic block. If you use a full-length peg here the mechanism will jam.

Fig.7.100 The worm gear installed

Fig.7.101 The driveshaft for the camera is installed next

Step 3 (Figures 7.100 and 7.101)

Now the drive shafts and associated parts are added, starting with the worm gear. The worm gear fits into the lower chamber of the main block. A 47-millimetre shaft is fitted with a 24-tooth gearwheel and the smallest size of pulley at one end. It is then threaded through the main block and the worm gear, and fixed in place using a "nut" added at the other end of the shaft (Figure 7.100). The 24-tooth gearwheel is fitted in the upper chamber of the main block. A 79-millimetre shaft is then threaded through the top of the block and this gearwheel, placing the gearwheel at the centre of the shaft. Two fixing "nuts" are then added to help keep everything in place (Figure 7.101).

Step 4 (Figures 7.102 to 7.105)

Next the camera is mounted on the drive assembly which is then fitted onto the front platform of the robot. Start by fitting black pegs into the bottom pair of holes in the camera, and the pair of holes immediately above these (Figure 7.102). Two angled 9 by 1 beams are then fitted onto the camera (Figure

Fig.7.102 The camera is mounted
via four pegs

Fig.7.103 The angle beams fitted
on the camera

7.103) and this assembly is then added onto the drive shaft (Figure 7.104). The whole assembly is then fitted onto the front platform of the robot (Figure 7.105).

Fig.7.104 The camera installed on
the drive shaft

Fig.7.105 The completed assembly
mounted on the front of
the robot

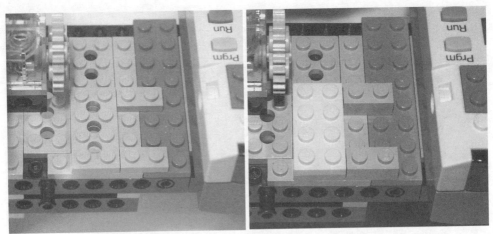

Fig.7.106 The initial stage of
the mounting pad

Fig.7.107 The completed pad

Step 6 (Figures 7.106 to 7.110)

The motor fits on the front platform of the robot to one side of the camera's mounting and drive assembly. A mounting pad for the motor is made from small plates, with a 4 by 1 plate, a 4 by 2 plate, and two 2 by 1 types being put in place first (Figure 7.106). Two more 2 by 1 plates and another 4 by 2 type are then added (Figure 7.107). This completes the mounting pad, and now the motor is fitted with an 8-tooth gearwheel and fitted onto the pad (Figure 7.108). Make sure that the gearwheel on the motor meshes properly with the one on the camera mounting. With a reduction ratio of 3 to 1 from the motor to the intermediate drive shaft, followed by a 24 to 1 reduction from here to the camera itself, there is a 72 to 1 reduction ratio overall. This makes it easy to control the camera with

Fig.7.108 The motor installed on
its mounting pad

good precision. To complete the robot the motor is connected to output B of the RCX unit (Figure 7.109). This gives the finished robot of Figure 7.110, which will respond in the correct fashion to the commands in the Vision Command programming language.

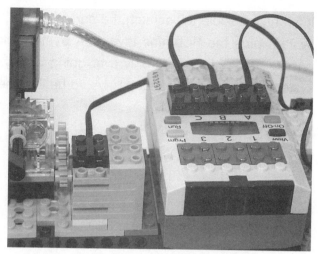

Fig.7.109 The motor is connected to output B of the RCX unit

Fig.7.110 The finished robot, complete with camera drive

It is only possible to "scratch the surface" here, and the Vision Command system plus the Robotics Invention System clearly has almost endless possibilities. If you were only ever going to buy one expansion set for the system, then I suppose that this would be the one to go for.

Appendix 1

Web addresses

There are numerous web sites devoted to various aspects of Lego products, including some that are specifically devoted to Lego MindStorms robots and programming the robots in various languages. Any good search engine should soon turn up a large number of interesting sites. The few sites mentioned here are likely to be especially useful.

www.legomindstorms.com

This is the official Lego MindStorms site, and as one would expect, it has all the latest news, projects to build, etc.

www.legoworldshop.com

This is an online shop that sells Lego kits, spares, additional sensors and motors, etc. Those living in the USA and Canada should use the Lego Shop-at-Home Service, which is a telephone based mail order service. The telephone numbers are 1-800-835-4386 (USA) and 1-800-267-5346 (Canada).

www.geocities.com/area51//nebula8488/lego.html

This is the source of PBrickCommand, the program mentioned in chapter 2. Even if you have Visual BASIC or VBA it is well worthwhile giving this freeware program a tryout.

www.lego.com/dacta/robolab

Robolab™ is an educational version of MindStorms software and is supplied by Commotion Ltd, Unit 11, Tannery Road, Tonbridge, Kent, TN9 1RF, telephone 01732-773399. Commotion Ltd. are suppliers of educational robotics materials. **Please Note.** Robolab software differs considerably from that supplied in the normal MindStorms RIS kit.

Appendix 2

Useful facts and figures

Sources for commands such as SetVal, IF, and While.

Number	Source selected
0	Variable
1	Timer
2	Constant
3	Motor status
4	Random
8	Program number
9	Sensor value
10	Sensor type
11	Sensor mode
12	Sensor (raw)
13	Sensor (Boolean)
14	Watch
15	PB Message

Relational operators in If and While commands.

Number	Operator
0	> (greater than)
1	< (less than)
2	= (equal to)
3	<> (not equal to)

Variables are numbered from 0 to 31 and can contain values from −32768 to +32767.

Constants can also contain values from −32768 to +32767.

There are four timers numbered from 0 to 3.

Sensor numbers from 0 to 2 refer to inputs 1 to 3 respectively of the RCX unit.

Output numbers from 0 to 2 refer to outputs 1 to 3 on the RCX unit.

Appendix 3

Immediate commands

AbsVar	InitComm
AlterDir	MemMap
AndVar	MulVar
BeginOfSub	Off
BeginOfTask	On
ClearEvent	OrVar
ClearSensorValue	PBAliveOrNot
ClearTimer	PBBattery
CloseComm	PBPowerDownTime
DatologNext	PBTurnOff
DeleteAllSubs	PBTxPower
DeleteAllTasks	PlaySystemSound
DeleteSub	PlayTone
DeleteTask	Poll
DivVar	SelectDisplay
DownloadFirmware	SelectPrgm
EndOfSub	SetDatalog
EndOfSubNoDownload	SetEvent
EndOfTask	SetFwd
EndOfTaskNoDownload	SetPower
Float	SetRwd
GetThreadPriority	SetSensorMode

SetSensorType

SetThreadPriority

SetVar

SetWatch

SgnVar

StartTask

StopAllTasks

StopTask

SubVar

SumVar

TowerAlive

TowerAndCableConnected

UnlockFirmware

UnlockPBrick

UploadDatalog

Appendix 4

Downloadable commands

AbsVar

AlterDir

AndVar

ClearPBMessage

ClearSensorValue

ClearTimer

DatologNext

DivVar

Else

EndIf

EndLoop

EndWhile

Float

Gosub

If

Loop

MulVar

Off

On

OrVar

PBTurnOff

PBTxPower

PlaySystemSound

PlayTone

SelectDisplay

SendPBMessage

SetFwd

SetPower

SetRwd

SetSensorMode

SetSensorType

SetVar

SetWatch

SgnVar

StartTask

StopAllTasks

StopTask

SubVar

SumVar

Wait

While

Appendix 5

Sensor modes and types

The SetSensorMode mode settings.

Number	Mode selected
0	Raw
1	Boolean
2	Transition counter (counts changes from 0 to 1 and 1 to 0)
3	Periodic counter (counts pulses)
4	Percent
5	Celsius
6	Fahrenheit
7	Angle

The SetSensorType type settings

Number	Type selected
0	None
1	Switch (touch sensor)
2	Temperature
3	Reflection (light sensor)
4	Angle (rotation sensor)

Appendix 6

Lego parts

In the U.K. Lego sensors, connector plates, etc. can be obtained from:

Commotion Ltd,

Unit 11

Tannery Road

Tonbridge

Kent

TN9 1RF

Tel. 01732 773399

Fax 01732 773390

Cat No.	Component
9886	Set of three electric plates
9897	Set of three connecting leads (three different sizes)
9756	Angle (rotation) sensor
9755	Temperature sensor
9757	Touch sensor
9758	Light sensor
5225	Reduction gear motor
23594-1	Small white plastic box
23595-1	Larger white plastic box

Appendix 7

Buying components

The electronic components used in the designs in this book should be available from any large electronic component retailer. These sources can also supply tools, wire, fixings, etc. This is a list of some web addresses of UK component retailers. Many have online catalogues and ordering facilities. Greenweld is a useful source of surplus mechanical, electrical and electronic goods which should be of interest to anyone building robots "from scratch".

Company	Web Address
ASR Components	www.asr.co.uk
Electrovalue Ltd	www.electrovalue.com
Greenweld	www.greenweld.co.uk
Maplin Electronics Ltd	www.maplin.co.uk
Premier Farnell	www.farnell.co.uk
Rapid Electronics	www.rapidelectronics.co.uk
Sky Electronics	www.skyelectronics.co.uk

Index